USING FERTILIZERS IN THE CULTURE OF CHRISTMAS TREES

BY

THOM J. McEVOY

ASSOCIATE PROFESSOR AND EXTENSION FORESTER
UNIVERSITY OF VERMONT

Paragon Books
RD 2, Box 3110
Hinesburg, VT 05461
802-482-3823

The drawing on the cover is used by permission of
High Reach Farm, St. Johnsbury, Vermont,
Steve Parker and Susanne Terry, principals.

The artist is Joanne Noyes of Kirby, Vermont.

FIRST EDITION

Copyright ©1992 by Paragon Books, Inc.
Printed in Vermont by
L. Brown & Sons Printing, Inc., East Montpelier.

ISBN 0-9631144-0-9

USING FERTILIZERS IN THE CULTURE OF CHRISTMAS TREES

TABLE OF CONTENTS
■■

0.1 PREFACE AND ACKNOWLEDGMENTS

I wrote this book for Christmas tree growers and their advisors to provide a more-than-introductory treatment of the subject of soil fertility and mineral nutrition in conifers. After nearly 12 years of advising growers on this subject, the task of assembling a compendium of information for those who want to understand the reasoning behind the recommendations of experts seemed like a good idea. Since most growers use fertilizers whether they need to or not, I am hoping the book will cause them to re-think their cultural practices.

I could never have spent the time pulling together the information for this book if I had not been awarded a sabbatical leave from my duties at the University of Vermont. I owe a debt of thanks to my colleagues there who saw fit to grant my leave request. I also want to thank the Forestry Department at the University of Florida for office space and secretarial support during my 12-month leave. Florida proved to be so thoroughly different from Vermont that I was able to disengage successfully and focus most of my energy on this book.

I also want to thank four people who reviewed the entire manuscript and offered many excellent comments and suggestions, almost all of which were incorporated into the final draft: Drs. John Ahrens, Plant Scientist at the Connecticut Agricultural Experiment Station and Christmas tree grower; Eric Jokela, Associate Professor and Silviculturist at the University of Florida; Alan Roberts, retired Professor of French Literature at Union College and a Christmas tree grower in Starksboro, Vermont; and Doug Lantagne, Associate Professor and Forest Regeneration Specialist, Michigan State University.

As I was writing this book, my feelings about it swung between a strong sense of worthiness and a dismal impression that the project was a waste of time. Although my opinion about it now is more the former than the later, the people who had to deal with my mood swings during the project deserve a special thanks—my wife Susan, daughters

Jessica and Kara, and my son Christopher—we call him Woogie—who was born two months before we went on leave.

I dedicate the book to Woogie because he reminded me on the dark days during the project that there are a lot of things other than this book that are worthwhile.

1.0 INTRODUCTION

Of all the knowledge required by a successful Christmas tree grower, fertilizer use is an area for which the least amount of information exists. Yet virtually all growers use fertilizers, mostly on the recommendations of experts or on the advice of peers. Since fertilizers are fairly inexpensive and easy to use, monitoring response and estimating cost efficiency is rarely a concern. Fertilizer efficacy for most growers who use the recommendations of others is a matter of faith rather than fact. Periodic fertilizer applications, even in the absence of observable responses, are often rationalized as a necessity—without them, trees will do poorly.

Although little information exists on fertilizer use in Christmas trees, a substantial amount of forestry research on mineral nutrition has been reported. Most studies, however, look at the effects of fertilizers and other soil amendments on growth factors that are of little concern to Christmas tree growers; factors like volume increment and diameter growth. With few exceptions, these studies are not generally applicable to the effects of fertilizers on factors like foliage density, color and appearance; although they help to define nutrient sufficiency in trees. A major purpose of this book is to relate some of the applicable research on forest tree nutrition to Christmas tree culture. There are also a few good fertilizer studies with Christmas trees that are described as well.

Christmas trees, unlike most annual crops, will usually "suffer a fool's folly" easily and are forgiving. Mistakes can be corrected. There is usually plenty of time during the 5–15 year rotation to adjust cultural techniques. However, as more and more people enter the business and the supply of trees increases, prices will decline and grower profits will follow. Profitability will depend more on production efficiency—keeping costs down and product quality high. Lost time and poor quality trees are more costly as markets become increasingly competitive.

Fertilizers can shorten rotations by accelerating tree growth. They can also improve foliage quality for many species. However, some sites do not require fertilizers, and some species do not respond to supplements enough to warrant their use.

Trees, and many of the conifers in particular—especially the pines—have a tremendous ability to utilize the nutrient supplying capacity of even the poorest soils. Known as "forage feeders", tree roots have evolved mechanisms and associations with other plants and animals that enable them to obtain soil nutrients very efficiently. This aspect more than any other differentiates trees from most agronomic crops—given adequate moisture and favorable temperatures just about any soil in the World will support trees of one species or another. On the other hand, most agronomic crops sacrifice adaptability for high yields, which are almost always dependent on high levels of fertility.

Even though most Christmas tree species are highly adaptable to a wide range of sites, judicious use of soil amendments or fertilizers will, in many circumstances, improve growing conditions. This is especially true when forest trees are planted in abandoned fields and other habitats that are far different from those in which they evolved. Since knowing what to apply, how much, and when to fertilize is usually a guess for most growers, another purpose of the book is to help take some of the guesswork out of fertilizer use.

There are many booklets available that teach the "A-to-Zs" of Christmas tree production, but most of them gloss over the subject of fertilizers. This book deals solely with mineral nutrition of conifers grown for Christmas trees and how fertilizers can be used to improve growing conditions and tree quality. It is a primer on tree growth, soils, and mineral nutrient behavior and uptake by roots. Covered in greater detail are descriptions of the fertilizer materials and how they are applied. Also discussed are important nutrient interactions, potential fertilizer responses of different Christmas tree species, and some practical aspects of using fertilizers in the plantation.

This book should be of greatest use to those growers and their advisors interested in tree nutrition and how to interpret the nutrient status of Christmas tree plantations from soil tests, foliar analyses and other observations. It is not a cookbook since there are no rules-of-thumb that apply in every circumstance. Growers who read the book must apply the information in a manner that fits their specific conditions.

2.0 THE CULTURAL OBJECTIVES OF GROWING CHRISTMAS TREES

Put simply, the goal of a Christmas tree grower is to produce the best tree possible in the shortest amount of time, keeping labor and material costs to a minimum. To achieve this end, there are at least five factors of importance to the grower that are influenced by mineral nutrition: 1) growth rate, 2) foliage color, 3) branch and foliage density, 4) vigor, and 5) needle retention. However, the condition of any of these factors is not controlled exclusively by mineral nutrition. Genetics plays a major role, but within a species there is also a great deal of interaction between factors—for example, vigorous trees usually show good color—and interactions with other practices employed by the grower; pruning or shearing mostly influences branch density, but bud formation has been shown to be strongly controlled by mineral nutrition. A discussion of each of these factors, how they are influenced by mineral nutrition, and interactions with other factors or practices employed by the grower will help put fertilizers in the proper perspective.

2.1 Growth Rate

The change in a tree's size, whether height, weight, girth or some other parameter, expressed as a function of time is a tree's growth rate (Figure 2-1). Most research on forest nutrition looks at changes in growth rate as a measure of response to fertilizer treatments. If trees are made to grow faster from the application of fertilizers, they are said to have "responded" to the treatment.

Unfortunately, traditional measures of growth are not meaningful for a Christmas tree grower even though the objective is to minimize the time between planting and harvest. A grower wants height growth, but not at the expense of branch and foliage density. Treatments that increase height growth must be countered with treatments that promote branching. Many growers feel as though the effects of fertilizers in the plantation are wasted because faster growth means more shearing. However, when used properly, fertil-

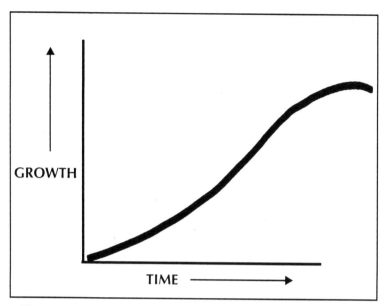

Figure 2-1. Trees grow slowly at first, then go through a period of accelerated growth. As the tree matures, growth slows down again. Christmas trees are usually harvested just as they enter the accelerated growth phase.

izers do not necessarily lead to extra shearing.

Of course, fertilizers do not cause growth—plants do not really "feed" on fertilizers. Increases in growth result from an increased rate of photosynthesis and/or a decreased rate of respiration.

Photosynthesis is the process whereby a tree manufactures complex carbohydrates—sugars—by using the sun's energy to combine carbon (C), hydrogen (H) and oxygen (O) in the proper proportions (Figure 2-2). The higher the rate of photosynthesis, the faster a tree will grow. Optimum nutrition will help maximize photosynthesis and growth rate, but since other conditions are involved, like moisture availability and light intensity, good mineral nutrition alone will not necessarily improve growth rate. Also, there is conflicting evidence regarding the direct influence of fertilizers on photosynthesis. Except in circumstances where a true nutrient deficiency exists and the process of photosynthesis is inhib-

PHOTOSYNTHEHSIS

$$CO_2 + H_2O + \text{Light Energy} \longrightarrow C_xH_{2x}O_x + O_2$$

RESPIRA TION

$$C_xH_{2x}O_x + O_2 \longrightarrow \text{Energy} + CO_2$$

Figure 2-2. Photosynthesis converts light energy into chemical energy and respiration converts sugars into energy tthat trees need to live.

ited by poor or unbalanced nutrition, the principal effect of fertilizers on photosynthesis may be physical. For example, greater light interception resulting from fertilizer-induced increases in leaf area may increase photosynthesis. Respiration is the expenditure of energy to carry on life-support systems. If respiration is high in relation to photosynthesis, growth is slower. Like photosynthesis, respiration is influenced by mineral nutrition, but not exclusively.

2.2 Foliage Color

Christmas tree consumers have shown a preference for dark green and blue green trees. With most species, dark green foliage is indicative of adequate nutrition. A yellowing of foliage, however, is usually one of the first signs of nutrient deficiency, although not always. Foliage color both within and between species is controlled by genetics. Some species and strains have a natural yellow-green appearance, that can become especially pronounced near the onset of dormancy, regardless of the nutrient status of the site. However, all things being equal, foliage color is a good indicator of the nutrient status of a tree. Sometimes, though, inadequate nutrient supply is not the cause of yellowing. Poor soil drainage can cause foliage to yellow even in the most fertile plantation.

Changing foliage color is one of the best reasons for using

fertilizers in the plantation. Nitrogen (N), discussed at length in the following sections, is one of the most influential elements on tree color. Severe deficiencies of some of the other elements will cause undesirable color changes as well.

2.3 Branch and Foliage Density

Within a species and variety, branch density is influenced by both shearing and mineral nutrition. Shearing truncates a branch forcing the development of buds that would otherwise remain dormant. Optimum nutrition increases branch elongation, but it also increases bud formation. Foliage density, which is the result of needle size and number, is strongly influenced by nutrition in many species.

2.4 Vigor

A vigorous tree is one that is almost perfectly tuned to its surroundings and growing well. Like a healthy person, a vigorous tree is capable of surviving stresses caused by pests, disease, weather and other influences. Adequate and balanced nutrition is an important determinant of vigor. Trees that lack vigor handle stresses poorly and are slow to recover when conditions improve.

Also, vigorous trees utilize supplemental nutrition more efficiently. It is easier to maintain and improve conditions in a plantation that is doing well, than in one where trees are failing due to poor or unbalanced nutrition and other causes.

2.5 Needle Retention

Growers often see the product of their efforts as trees stacked along the roadside awaiting transport to market. But the product is still many days from the consumer. Although needle retention is controlled to a large extent by genetics, within a species and strain nutrition and handling after harvest can determine how quickly needles will fall. Good nutrition will not overcome the effects of poor handling but it may improve needle retention. However, the relationship of foliage shedding to nutrition is not clearly established, and in some cases researchers have suggested there is no relationship.

In most circumstances it is impossible to achieve the best trees, minimizing time and labor inputs, without amending the natural fertility of the soil. Christmas trees are usually planted on infertile sites. Although conifers are capable of growing on even the poorest of sites, soil amendments can substantially improved the ability of these areas to grow Christmas trees. However, indiscriminate use of fertilizers can cause more harm than good. In agriculture, fertilizers are applied according to crop requirements necessary to achieve a certain yield. The same reasoning is valid with Christmas trees, but needs and response goals are not always easy to establish. A grower who uses fertilizers must learn to assess response and adjust fertilizer applications accordingly. Measuring fertilizer response is the subject of section 8.4.

3.0 HOW CONIFERS GROW

On an evolutionary scale conifers are a very primitive group of plants. Analysis of pollen preserved in bogs and fossil evidence suggests that the conifers evolved before most hardwood tree species. As a result, conifers tend to be simpler in structure and function than hardwoods and more adaptable to a wider range of site conditions.

Conifers are excellent competitors on harsh sites, but many also do extremely well on better sites in the absence of competition from hardwoods. Generally speaking, those conifer species adapted to harsh, nutrient-poor sites tend to respond less to soil amendments than those adapted to better sites. Also, species with very wide site tolerances, like Scots pine, do not respond so readily to fertilizer treatments as do species with more narrow site requirements, like white pine or balsam fir.

The pines, spruces and firs are the principal genera used for Christmas tree culture in the U.S. Each group is composed of species that have two things in common: 1) they produce an unprotected or "naked" seed in cones at maturity (hence the name conifer), and 2) their leaves are needles that persist for more than one growing season (hence the common name "evergreen"). These species also exhibit a pattern of "primary" growth (stem and branch elongation) that is intermittent. Periods of growth, or flushing, are followed by periods of rest or dormancy. Generally, in the north and at high elevations there is one growth flush each year in the spring, during which resting buds are formed for over-wintering. However, some northern species like jack pine are capable of multiple flushes when conditions are favorable.

Secondary growth refers to increases in the girth of branches and stems. Although this type of growth is more important for most forestry objectives, it is not nearly so important to the Christmas tree grower as primary growth which largely determines the shape and extent of foliage.

In the South, pines exhibit intermittent but recurring primary growth. Periods of flushing are followed by rest periods of varying duration. The extent of flushing and length of rest is largely controlled by environmental conditions (65*). Trees may flush four or five times during a year. However, there is usually one resting period during the winter months that is typically longer than the others. The extent of flushing, in addition to being controlled by environmental conditions, is also controlled by the length of the resting period. Successive flushes after a long resting period are smaller as resting periods are shorter.

Intermittent primary growth in conifers appears to be a strategy that enables trees to take advantage of favorable conditions or, possibly, to survive when conditions are less favorable. Fertilizer applications, especially with nitrogen when moisture and temperatures are favorable, will encourage flushing. A grower must shear the elongated stem and branches of older trees after each flush to obtain dense foliage and a conical form.

Late-season applications of nitrogen-containing fertilizers to some northern species when growing conditions are favorable may encourage flushing of buds that should have remained closed for the winter. Frost damage is almost assured if northern trees flush for a second time after the middle of July. The new foliage, with its complement of buds, does not have adequate time to harden-off before freezing temperatures set in. Fortunately, late-season flushes in northern species are rare.

Roots are usually the first tissues to start or accelerate growth in the spring. In warm regions, roots never stop growing. Depending upon ground conditions and soil temperatures in the North, roots may begin growing 2–4 weeks before buds start to expand (32). Leader growth from expanding buds is usually rapid initially but tapers off by late June in the North. Root growth slows during the middle of summer, probably as a response to high temperature and moisture deficits, but it picks up again in the fall with favorable temperatures and moisture. After the first few frosts, root growth will slow and stop altogether when the ground freezes.

---

*Numbers in parentheses correspond to sources of literature cited. These sources are listed in alphabetical order in Appendix C.

The structure and function of conifer roots is discussed in section 6.1.

Conifers can be sheared to obtain almost any form by varying the length to which branches are allowed to grow. Good fertility increases bud formation but it also increases elongation of flushed branch leaders. Too much nitrogen will result in long and leggy branches. As mentioned earlier, branch length is controlled by shearing, and if it is done correctly, buds will form around the terminal end of the branch. The effect with frequent shearing is a pattern of branching that increases from the main stem outward. Typically, Christmas trees are shaped so that the width at the base of the tree is 60–80% of tree height. The proportion varies between species.

4.0 THEORIES OF PLANT NUTRITION

The positive effects of soil amendments on plants have been known since before the time of Christ. Over the years numerous theories of plant nutrition have evolved, and many have since been refuted. However, there are three that provide a foundation for contemporary thinking on the subject—the law of the minimum, the law of diminishing returns, and nutrient balancing.

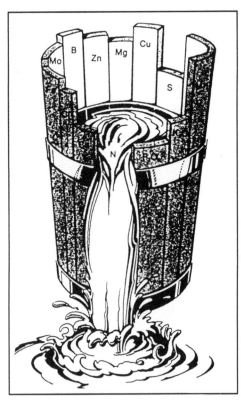

Figure 4-1. A barrel can only hold as much as its shortest stave will allow. Increase the length of that stave and another will limit the capacity. Managing soil fertility is an attempt to increase the supply of nutrients that are most limiting. Used with permission of "The Fertilizer Handbook," published by The Fertilizer Institute, Washington, DC.

4.1 Law of the Minimum

One of the first theories of plant nutrition to survive the test of time is the "law of the minimum". Originally proposed by Justis von Liebig (1803–1873), it says in effect that plant growth is controlled by the element in shortest supply (Figure 4-1). When that element is provided in optimum quantities, a shortage of another element will limit growth. The central idea of this theory is that there is always a shortage of something and a tree will respond only to treatments that improve the supply of the element in question. Increasing the availability of other nutrients will not increase growth, even though they may be taken up and stored by the plant. This idea also applies to non-nutrient growth factors, like temperature and water availability.

Liebig's law demonstrates why blanket applications of fertilizers with no knowledge of the natural fertility of a site is often wasteful and sometimes damaging. It also points out that optimum nutrition is more a function of the total nutrient supplying capacity of a site and not just the supply of any given element. However, correctly identifying the element in short supply is not always easy, especially since excesses of one nutrient can cause deficiencies of another. A discussion of this phenomenon, known as nutrient interactions, is found in section 11.0.

4.1.1 Luxury Consumption

The law of the minimum suggests that the nutrient status of a Christmas tree plantation is not solely the product of

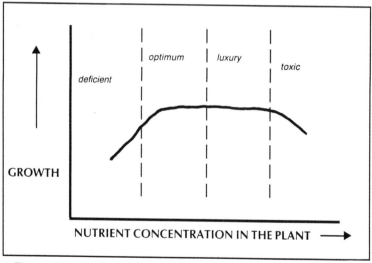

Figure 4-2. When increasing nutrient concentration does not increase growth the tree is consuming luxury quantities of the element in question.

nutrient supplies. In fact, when a plant is supplied with quantities of an element beyond that which it requires for optimum growth, under certain conditions and with some elements, the plant will take up far more of the element than it needs. This phenomenon is known as "luxury consumption", implying that it is a luxury for the plant to have more than is optimally required. Any time an element is supplied to, and taken up by, a plant with no visible response, it is considered luxury consumption.

The concept of luxury consumption is often depicted on a continuum that extends from deficiency to toxicity (Figure 4-2). The point of adequate nutrition is bracketed by conditions where shortages or excesses of a particular element are difficult to diagnose. Potassium is an element that virtually all plants will consume in luxury quantities. Hence, the potassium status of plants is difficult to determine.

4.2 Law of Diminishing Returns

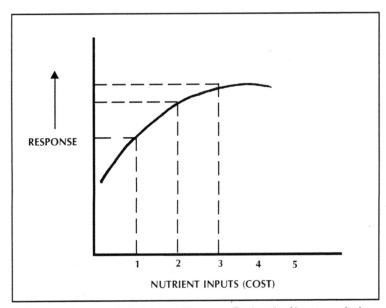

Figure 4-3. Law of Diminishing Returns. Each unit of input results in less response. Three units will provide the miximum response, but the proportional cost of the last unit is very high.

A second theory that has stood the test of time was proposed by E.A. Mitscherlich in 1909. His "law of diminishing returns" suggests that the response from fertilizer applications diminishes with each increment, up to the point where there is no response or a negative response resulting from mineral toxicities. (Figure 4-3). Although recently refuted in some respects, Mitscherlich's law nevertheless clearly shows the economics of soil amendment. The cost per unit of response increases as the amount of fertilizers increase. In other words, the efficiency of the treatment decreases. With limited dollars for fertilizers and other cultural practices, a grower must decide the level of efficiency that is most reasonable and profitable. Another important idea suggested by this theory is that there are limits to which a poor site can be improved, and good sites may not need amendments.

4.3 Nutrient Balancing

Both Liebig's and Mitscherlich's ideas led to a theory of plant nutrition which is not so easily defined as to be summarized in a "law". In fact, it is not even clear who first proposed the idea, but a contemporary Swedish scientist, Torsten Ingestad, is to be credited with demonstrating its validity. Interestingly, many of his experiments have involved the use of conifer seedlings grown in carefully controlled nutrient solutions.

The theory suggests that a factor in plant nutrition which is even more important than absolute quantities of nutrients in the soil is the balance of supply of one nutrient to another. Furthermore, Ingestad has discovered that this balance is very similar for a diverse collection of plants (25). When the supply of essential nutrients is expressed as a ratio to nitrogen, and the proper balance is established, relative growth rate becomes a function of nitrogen supply up to the point of optimum. Even trees growing under extremely nutrient-poor conditions will establish a balance, never growing faster than the supply of nutrients allows. This explains why forest trees do quite well on nutrient-poor sites.

Three important ideas emerge from the theory of balanced nutrition. First, to ignore the concept, even in the case of adequate nutrient supplies, is to run the risk of creating deficiencies because the supply of one element is way out of proportion to another. For example, high levels of calcium may cause a potassium deficiency even though soil potassium levels are adequate. Other antagonistic relationships exist as well and are discussed in section 11.0.

Second, when a balance has been achieved, and growth rate is maximized, with the exception of nitrogen, further nutrient additions are required to replace only those amounts that have been harvested. This point underscores the fact that soils are fertilized, not trees, and over time a soil's ability to supply essential nutrients can be improved with fertilizers.

Finally, the theory implies that the best means of deciding when things are in balance is to analyze the nutrient content of the foliage and adjust the fertility program accordingly. Section 8.0 is devoted to the subjects of soil testing and foliar analysis.

The premise of this book on using fertilizers in the Christmas tree plantation rests mostly on the theory of balanced nutrition. The ideas about balanced nutrition proposed by Ingestad and others will be expanded upon and referred to constantly in the sections that follow.

5.0 UNDERSTANDING SOILS

Since fertilizers are most often applied to the soil, some basic knowledge of soil properties is essential to the Christmas tree grower. An adequate evaluation of soil characteristics in the plantation should occur months before tree planting.

Important aspects to consider are: soil depth, texture and structure, soil reaction (pH) and natural fertility. The best means of assessing these factors is by observation and testing, the subject of section 8.1. Also, the county Soil Conservation Service (SCS) may be able to offer useful information about a particular soil type.

5.1 Soil depth

Most Christmas tree species do not need a tremendous volume of soil in which to grow over the course of a short rotation, but they do require enough soil to gain a foothold. Often soil depth is restricted by an impervious layer below the surface that causes poor drainage. Standing water is more apt to be the problem in these circumstances than a lack of soil. These sites can be easily avoided using information from the county SCS Soil Survey Maps (see Figure 8-1). Soil depth in and of itself does not have much to do with fertility, except when shallow soils restrict the rooting potential of trees. However, most Christmas tree species, especially the pines, are adapted to well-drained site conditions. Some species are more opportunistic than others, having a wider range of site conditions on which they will grow. Therefore, on soils with imperfect drainage species selection must be carefully matched to the site.

5.2 Texture and Structure

The texture of a soil refers to the relative proportions of sand, silt and clay, while structure refers to the aggregation of particles in the soil (Figure 5-1).

Indirectly, soil texture has a tremendous influence on natural fertility because it implies something about its chemical nature, especially how it will react to fertilization. Generally speaking, coarse textured soils are well-drained and nutrient-poor. The reason for this is that coarse soils are fairly inert and lack a favorable chemistry for nutrient retention. The result—nutrients wash right through when it rains. Trees growing on a coarse textured soil will respond to fertilization, however the effect is often short-lived. A suc-

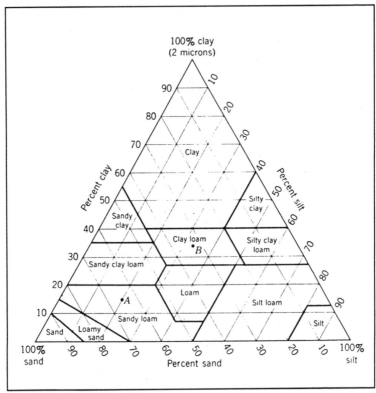

Figure 5-1. The textural triangle shows the limits of sand, silt, and clay contents of the various texture classes. Point A represents a soil that contains 65 percent sand, 15 percent clay, and 20 percent silt, and is a sandy loam. Used with permission of the California Fertilizer Association.

cessful fertilization strategy in this circumstance is to apply fertilizers lightly but often.

Mineral nutrients exist in the soil either as salts or, when dissociated by water, as charged ions (Figure 5-2). It is the positively or negatively charged nutrient ions that plants use.

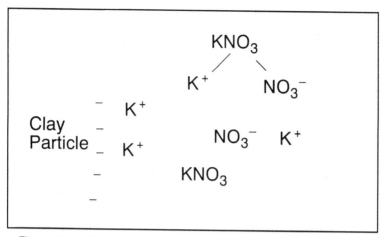

Figure 5-2. Mineral nutrients exist in the soil as salts or as ions attached to soil particles or in solution. Potassium nitrate (KNO_3) will dissociate into positive and negative ions.

If a soil is not able to provide adequate sites for these free-floating ions, holding them for use by plants, they are quickly lost to leaching. The "cation exchange capacity" is a common measure of a soil's nutrient retention capabilities. Fine textured soils, composed of silt and clay, are not as well- drained but tend to be more fertile, or have a higher capacity for good fertility because they have a higher cation exchange capacity (Figure 5-3).

Soil particles have a predominantly negative charge. As a result, fine-textured soils have more negatively charged sites and a higher cation exchange capacity than coarse soils. One of the reasons for this is that fine-textured soils, clays in particular, have many times more particle surface area than do coarse soils.

The structure of a soil refers to the way particles are aggregated. It is more a description of the physical characteristics of the soil than its chemistry. Soils with good structure usually have higher proportions of silt and clay to sand. They are also soils that have a good supply of organic matter and an adequate supply of calcium. On clay soils, good structure improves aeration and drainage. On sandy soils good struc-

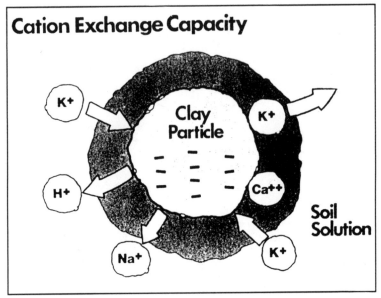

Cation Exchange Capacity

Figure 5-3. Schematic illustration of the exchange of cations between the negatively charged clay particles and the soil solution. By permission of the California Fertilizer Association.

ture will improve the water-holding capacity. Organic matter, in addition to improving structure, also increases cation exchange capacity and moisture retention.

5.3 Soil Reaction (pH)

The reaction of a soil is a measure of its acidity or basicity, expressed as the logarithm (base 10) of the reciprocal of the hydrogen ion (H^+) concentration. Hence, the higher the H^+ ion concentration, the lower the pH and the more acid a soil is.

$$pH = \log 1/H^+$$

Ions are rarely without a counterbalancing mate that carries an opposite charge. This is especially important to remember because fertilizers are salts of mated ions. In the case of hydrogen, the mate is the negatively charged hydroxyl ion (OH^-). When H^+ and OH^- combine they form water (HOH or H_2O). Pure water is a perfect match of mates—the number of H^+ ions equals the number of OH^- ions—and is neutral. When there are more H^+ ions than OH^- the solution is acid; when the reverse is true the solution is said to be basic.

Soil pH is expressed on a logarithmic scale as a value between 1 and 14 (Figure 5-4). The lower the number the higher the acidity, by a factor of 10. The logarithmic scale is used because the distance between values on an absolute scale would be too large to be of any practical use. Seven is neutral—neither acid or basic—(pure water), and the higher the number, the more basic the soil. A soil with a pH of 5.0 is 10 times more acid than a soil with a pH of 6.0, and 100 times more acid than a soil with a pH of 7.0.

An accurate measure of soil reaction, or pH, is indispensable to the Christmas tree grower using fertilizers. Soil pH affects the availability of most of the nutrient ions by causing those with positive charges (also known as cations) to leach under acid conditions, and negatively charged ions (called anions) to be locked-up when a soil is too basic. Also, different tree species have different pH requirements.

In an acid soil, the negatively charged exchange sites on

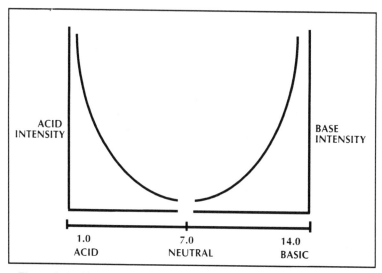

Figure 5-4. pH is a logarithmic scale between 1 and 14. Less than 7 is acid and more than 7 is basic. The optimum for most Christmas trees is between 5 and 6.

soil particles are covered with tenaciously held cations of iron (Fe^{++}) and aluminum (Al^{+++}). Nutrient cations like potassium (K^+) and magnesium (Mg^{++}), without mates on soil particles, leach through the soil. Under basic soil conditions, strong free cations of Al^{+++} and Fe^{++} combine with nutrient anions locking them up and making them unavailable for plants. Soil pH is a very delicate balance that has a tremendous bearing on the health and productivity of the Christmas tree plantation. Most of the conifers prefer acid to slightly acid conditions (a pH of 5.0–6.0 by the soil-in-water method).

Soil pH determination is discussed further in section 8.1.1. The soil reaction preferences of some commercially important Christmas tree species is found in section 12.0.

Soils in humid areas of the country tend to be acid and may need to have the pH raised, while soils in more arid regions tend to be basic and may need to have the pH lowered. This is a very general rule, however, since soil reaction is more a function of the parent material of the soil and its history of land use in a particular area than climate.

Soil pH is a measure of acid intensity. It does not reveal anything about the amount of acid in a soil. Consider the analogy of two vessels, one large and the other small, filled with water of the same temperature. To change the temperature in the vessels an equal amount, it would require more energy to do so in the larger than the smaller vessel. Temperature in this analogy is the same as pH. The amount of energy required to change temperature is analogous to what is known as the "buffer capacity" of the soil. Buffer capacity is a measure of a soil's ability to resist a change in pH. As a general rule, the more finely textured a soil (eg. clay), the higher its buffer capacity. A sandy soil of the same pH, with a much lower buffer capacity, will require considerably less base- or acid-forming agents to effect a change in pH than would a clay soil. Cation exchange capacity is approximately the same as buffer capacity.

A soil's reaction is changed by additions of lime to raise the pH, or by additions of sulfur or other acid-forming salts to lower the pH. A discussion of methods and material used to change soil pH is found in sections 8.1.1, 9.6 and 10.4.

5.4 Natural Fertility

Soils vary tremendously in fertility. For this reason it is impossible to develop an optimum and efficient fertilization program without knowing something about the natural fertility of the site. Information about soil parent material, texture, pH, organic matter content and buffer capacity give a good indication of fertility. This information is obtained through soil testing, the subject of section 8.1.

Knowledge of a site's natural fertility enables the grower to develop a program of fertilization that supplements the nutrient- supplying capability of the soil. Also, with baseline information, the grower is able to build site fertility over the years. As soil fertility increases, the response to and need for fertilization decreases (Figure 5-5). Some sites with some species may not require any supplemental fertilization, especially during the first rotation.

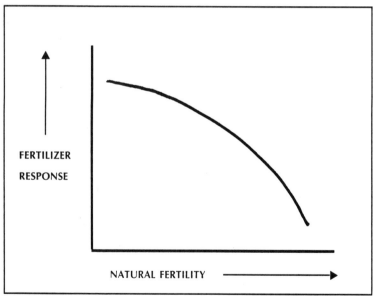

Figure 5-5. Fertilizer response will decrease as natural fertility of the site increases.

6.0 NUTRIENT UPTAKE IN THE PLANTATION

Although fertilizers are easy to use, their reactions in soil and uptake by plants is a fairly complicated matter. Thousands of scientist-years of research have been devoted to the study of how plants obtain and use nutrients from the soil. A thorough treatment of the subject of nutrient uptake is far beyond the scope of this book. However, a brief discussion of tree roots and their role in nutrition is in order.

6.1 Root Structure and Function

In addition to providing anchorage and a means of water uptake, roots also mine the soil for nutrients. These last two functions—water and nutrient uptake—are so important that the distribution of these resources in the soil will determine both the extent and pattern of rooting. For example, although root elongation is usually 2–3 times greater in sandy than clay soils, root mass and volume is often less in nutrient poor, wet or excessively dry soils. Adequate moisture and nutrition will promote strong rooting. However, after seedling establishment on a good site, favorable moisture and fertility promote shoot growth over root growth (51).

Depending upon the species and site in question, roots account for about 20% of a tree's mass, and 10–15% of a tree's total nutrient pool (51). On good sites, roots tend to be branchy and compact. Generally speaking, the drier and more nutrient-poor a site, the more extensive the root system and the higher the proportion of roots to above-ground parts. Intuitively this makes sense–when moisture and nutrients are scarce, a tree must devote more of its energy in pursuit of these resources. On the other hand, when water and nutrient supplies are adequate root systems tend to be more compact and above-ground parts proportionally larger.

In most circumstances, the lateral extent of the majority of tree roots is slightly greater than the width of the crown, also known as the "drip line" (Figure 6-1). On a poor, dry site, the lateral extent of roots is often greater. A 20-year-old Scots pine growing on a sandy soil can develop a lateral root

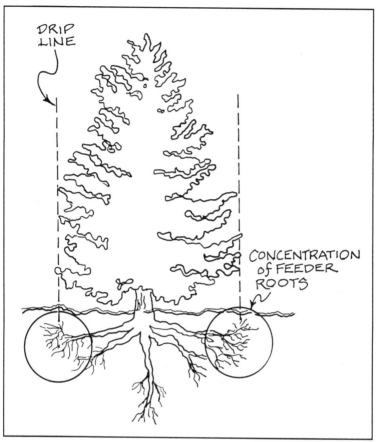

Figure 6-1. The feeder roots of a tree extend beyond the drip-line of the crown.

system that is up to 7 times the tree's height (31). On moist, well-drained sites, tree roots may occupy most of the land area in Christmas tree plantations after 4 to 5 years. However, roots are concentrated in tree rows.

As a group, the conifers tend to be more shallow rooted than hardwoods. This may be an adaptation to drier, nutrient-poor sites since these conditions are known to promote shallow rooting in forests. Even so, under normal circumstances up to 80% of the volume of a tree's roots is in the upper 8 inches of soil (31). Most of the "feeder roots" or fine roots that are responsible for nutrient uptake are found near the soil surface. These fine roots also support structures known as "root hairs" that form just behind a growing root tip (Figure 6-2). Root hairs increase the surface area of a root dramatically and are primarily responsible for water and nutrient absorption. Unfortunately, fine roots and root hairs are also very delicate. Soil compaction, and excessive amounts of salts and other chemicals, can kill them or severely limit their nutrient-uptake abilities.

Christmas tree growers need to be especially mindful of fertilizer placement. Heavy doses of a fertilizer with a high

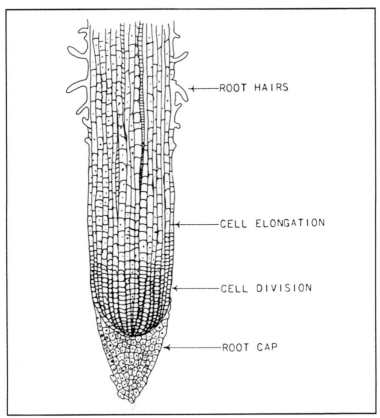

Figure 6-2. A microscopic view of a root tip. Used with permission of California Fertilizer Association.

salt index concentrated on top of roots will cause damage to the root system and "burning" of the foliage. Placement and timing of fertilizer applications is discussed in section 10.0.

Often the form of a tree's root system is a function of how a seedling was planted. Roots will tend to grow in the direction they were placed at planting. When planting machines are used, the root tips tend to point down the row, opposite the direction of machine travel (Figure 6-3). Knowing the pattern of root placement can afford the grower some efficiency advantages on fertilizer placement, especially during the first few years of the rotation.

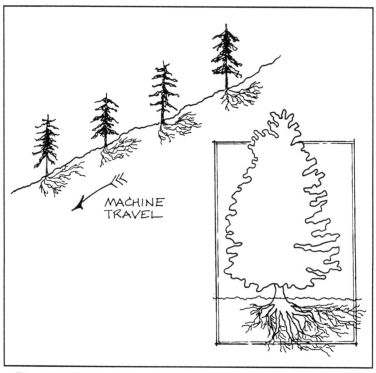

Figure 6-3. Roots tend to grow down a row, opposite the direction of machine travel.

6.1.1 Mycorrhizae

Many plants, but especially trees, have evolved a very specialized relationship with certain species of soil fungi. These fungi are nonpathogenic; in other words, they do not cause disease. The association is symbiotic—both the plant and the fungi benefit—and is known as "mycorrhizae". Mycorrhizae-forming fungi produce a mantle or sheath around and/or within the root that increases the surface-area of the roots many times. This increased surface-area, coupled with other biochemical root- fungus interactions that are not completely understood, enable the plant to take up water and nutrients more efficiently.

Mycorrhizae-forming fungi utilize carbohydrate from the roots as a source of energy and the plant gets the benefit of a more efficient root system. These plant-fungus associations may be the principal reason why trees can survive even under extremely nutrient-poor conditions. Adequate phosphorus nutrition in forest stands has been linked to mycorrhizae associations.

Mycorrhizae do exist in the Christmas tree plantation, especially in soils that once supported forests. However, some agricultural soils may be lacking in the appropriate species of fungi. Fortunately, many seedling nurseries will inoculate their stock with the proper fungi before lifting. It is important to note, however, that heavy fertilizer use will inhibit mycorrhizae development (34, 40), especially when applications are unbalanced (i.e. excessive doses of one nutrient without supplies of the others). High doses of nitrogen have been known to inhibit the formation of mycorrhizal roots (40).

6.2 Mechanisms of Nutrient Uptake

Tree roots must come into contact with nutrient ions in order to take them up. There are three means by which ions come into contact with roots: 1) contact exchange—the root exchanges an ion like hydrogen with a nutrient ion, like potassium, attached to a soil particle, without K^+ having to go into solution, 2) diffusion—as the roots take up the various ions a gradient is established—like a siphon—that results in continuous movement of ions toward the root surface, and 3) mass movement—during the course of water uptake, nutrient ions reach the root by being in solution with water. In this case it is the movement of water that creates the siphoning effect, not an ionic gradient. Phosphorus and potassium reach the root surfaces mostly through diffusion, while nitrate nitrogen (NO_3), calcium and magnesium use mass movement (55).

Once a nutrient ion comes into contact with the root, the ion is either passively absorbed into the root stream by ion exchange or diffusion (essentially the same processes as 1 and 2 in the preceding paragraph), or ions are actively absorbed (through an expenditure of energy) into root cells by the action of "carriers" or ion-binding compounds (55).

Active absorption helps explain why some ions are taken up selectively by roots.

Ion absorption has been the subject of many research projects in plant nutrition. The details are very complex and beyond the scope of this chapter. However, it is important for growers to realize that: 1) mineral nutrients are either positively or negatively charged ions, 2) these ions move in the soil, some more than others depending upon soil chemistry, and 3) roots have developed a specialized process to selectively absorb nutrients that the plant requires. Also important to remember, most commercial fertilizers are salts and excessive quantities will kill roots and damage foliage. Plantation trees should grow into areas of soil that have been enriched by fertilizers. Roots should not have to recover from fertilizer applications before the tree can take advantage of them.

7.0 THE ESSENTIAL NUTRIENTS

There are 16 elements that have been identified as "essential" for plant growth (Figure 7-1). The word "essential" means that an element has a functional role in plant nutrition; for some of the elements to the extent that their absence, or less than adequate amounts, will prevent or limit plant growth. Elements that are required in relatively large quantities are known as macronutrients, and those used in only very small quantities are called micronutrients.

Of the nine macronutrients, three—carbon (C), hydrogen (H) and oxygen (O)—are used in very large quantities as the principal components of carbohydrates—the product of photosynthesis. The plant obtains C from carbon dioxide (CO_2)

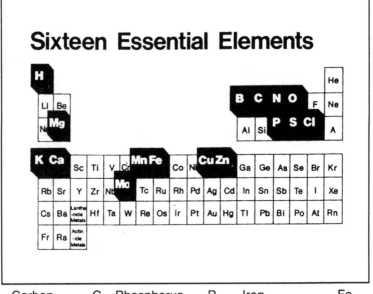

Sixteen Essential Elements

Carbon	C	Phosphorus	P	Iron	Fe
Hydrogen	H	Magnesium	Mg	Copper	Cu
Oxygen	O	Calcium	Ca	Boron	B
Nitrogen	N	Sulfur	S	Chlorine	Cl
Potassium	K	Manganese	Mn	Molybdenum	Mo

Figure 7-1. Periodic table of elements highlighting the 16 essential plant nutrients. Used with permission of the California Fertilizer Association.

in the atmosphere, and O and H from soil water. These elements are not obtained from the organic or mineral portions of the soil so they are not considered to be mineral nutrients. Also, because of the abundance of these elements, supply problems do not exist as they do for the remaining 13 that the plant must obtain from the soil.

Soil oxygen, although not a mineral nutrient, is a special case because it is essential for root respiration and can be limiting. If soil conditions eliminate oxygen, trees will suffer regardless of site fertility. Wet soils, or soils that have been compacted eliminating air space, will cause foliage yellowing that can not be corrected except with practices that improve soil aeration. Also, trees rooted in compacted or wet soils are stressed and more susceptible to root-rotting fungi.

7.1 Macronutrients

There are 6 mineral nutrients that a plant must obtain in relatively large quantities, sufficient to sustain growth and development. Various combinations of these six are often the principal components of mixed fertilizers. They are: nitrogen (N), potassium (K), phosphorus (P), calcium (Ca), magnesium (Mg) and sulfur (S). The first three—N, P and K—are sometimes referred to as "primary nutrients;" the second three—Ca, Mg and S—as "secondary nutrients." This terminology reflects the fact that the quantities used by trees, and the probability of obtaining a response with applications, are higher for the primary nutrients. The secondary nutrients are no less important but they are used in comparatively smaller quantities. A description of the role of each of these elements in plant nutrition follows. They are discussed in descending order of the amounts used by trees.

7.1.1 Nitrogen

Nitrogen is used by plants in quantities greater than any other element obtained from the soil, yet it is most often the nutrient that is in shortest supply. This is especially surprising since 75% of the atmosphere by volume is N and about 36,000 tons of N exist in gaseous form over each acre (63). However, atmospheric N represents only about 2% of the total on earth. Most N is tied up in rock, but in extremely low concentrations (8). On the earth's surface, the top 6–8 inches of soil holds the highest concentrations of N—about 1,500 parts per million (ppm). Less than 2% of this is held in forms that are available to plants, so N is usually in short supply for at least a portion of the growing season on all but the richest sites. Fine textured-soils may contain up to 10 times more N than coarse soils. Soils low in organic matter are usually N-poor soils.

Virtually all of the naturally occurring N used by plants is obtained from the soil where organic forms of N, principally plant and animal proteins, are converted by microorganisms to mineralized forms that are available to plants. Small amounts of atmospheric N are added to this by the action of soil bacteria that fix elemental N from the soil air, and from modest amounts that fall to earth with rain. Some non-coniferous species such as those in the legume family (eg., alder) have developed specialized symbiotic (ie. both organisms benefit) relationships with bacteria that infect their roots. The bacteria fix elemental N in exchange for a share of photosynthate produced by the plant. However, atmospheric sources of N are of little practical value to the Christmas tree grower, although in some areas of the country inputs from the combustion of fossil fuels can be fairly high.

There are principally two forms of soil N available to plants—ammonium, which exists as a cation (NH_4^+), and nitrate which exists as an anion (NO_3^-). Because of its positive charge, ammonium will be mated with the negative charges on soil particles, provided the soil is not too acidic. However, nitrate is a free floating ion that is subject to leaching with rainfall. Christmas tree species use both forms of N, however there is a chance that they will not do as well if only NO_3 is present. When conditions are favorable, soil bacteria will convert NH_4 to NO_3. This process is known as nitrification or mineralization.

Two common types of N fertilizers are salts of these two ions, mated with other ions of opposite charge, or mated together as NH_4NO_3—ammonium nitrate.

Fertilizer sources of N is the subject of section 9.1.

Nitrogen plays an important role in plant nutrition. It is involved in the formation of proteins, especially functional enzymes that control metabolic activities (55). It is also a component of chlorophyll, the molecules within which photosynthesis takes place. N's role in plant nutrition has been studied more than any other element. The irony of vast atmospheric and mineral quantities of N, coupled with the fact that it is frequently a growth-limiting factor, makes its supply and use by plants an interesting dilemma for scientists.

When N is supplied to deficient soils response usually takes the form of: 1) a distinct greening of yellow or light green foliage, or a darkening of already green leaves, and 2) an often dramatic and occasionally troublesome increase in the elongation of terminal leaders and lateral branches. When the response causes gangling leaders that are way out of proportion to the rest of the tree the effect is known as "over-stimulation". This symptom is usually an excellent indicator of too much N. Of all the essential elements, N is the only one that causes over-stimulation. However, leader growth can be controlled by shearing, and since shearing is a regular event in the plantation it matters little whether 1 inch or 6 inches is removed. A greater hazard of excessive N is burning of foliage, root damage and growth suppression. Excess N can also pollute ground-water supplies.

Nitrogen has a much greater effect on the growth of the above-ground parts of trees than roots (8). In addition to marked color changes and stem elongation, N has also been shown to increase the number and size of buds in the second year after application (16, 45, 53, 54) and foliage density— needle size, numbers of needles per unit of stem length and number of branches per whorl (6, 7, 35, 47, 48). An adequate supply of N increases growth rate in conifers (height, stem diameter and mass), but also makes the foliage more palatable to browsing animals and insects. Adequate and higher than adequate levels of N in plant tissue may also increase the susceptibility of some conifer species to diseases (20). However, it should be pointed out that increased disease susceptibility may be more a result of nutrient imbalance than absolute levels of N in the tissue. Also, there are numerous interactions between N and other elements in the soil and in the plant that affect N availability and utilization. These are discussed further in the section 11.0.

7.1.2 Potassium

Potassium, second only to N in terms of amounts used by plants, is a fairly common element of many minerals. Hence, like N, it is present in most soils in large quantities but is often tied up in minerals and unavailable to plants. Fine-textured soils made up of K-bearing minerals like micas and feldspars may have many thousands of pounds of available K per acre, while coarse-textured sands of silica and quartzite may have almost none. Generally, areas of high rainfall, coarse sandy soils and soils derived mostly from marine deposits are low in K, while areas of moderate rainfall, fine textured clay soils and soils derived from geologically younger parent material have adequate, occasionally more than adequate, levels of K (55). Trees use only about one-third as much K as N.

Only soil K that is already in solution or held loosely on the charged surface of soil particles is readily available to plants. However, as available K is taken up, previously unavailable K will take its place. Most tree species, and especially the conifers, can utilize this natural K-pool very readily without supplemental applications. There are very few instances of growth responses attributable to K applications. However, in some instances even on soils that have adequate supply, applications of K in combination with other elements will enhance plant response to fertilization. Abandoned agricultural lands, favorite sites for Christmas tree plantations, may be K-poor sites. The only way to ascertain this is through soil testing. Even though K-poor sites may be able to provide the needs of the plantation, when other nutrients are applied, K levels will need to be raised as well.

There is only one form of K used by plants—a cation with a single positive charge (K^+). Since it is only weakly held on the surface of soil particles and salts of K will go readily into solution, it is subject to leaching especially in acid soils with a low cation exchange capacity. Excessive calcium (Ca) usually found in high-pH soils will also cause K losses. In some clay soils with a high cation exchange capacity, K can get locked-up in minerals.

Potassium is the only macro-nutrient that is not a constituent of organic molecules. Rather, it remains in ionic form and its function is to mediate chemical reactions (37, 55). It also regulates the function of stomata—sausage-shaped cells on the undersides of needles where the exchange of gases takes place during photosynthesis, respiration and water transpiration.

Of the macro-nutrients, K may be the nutrient for which it is most difficult to establish need in Christmas tree culture. Severe deficiencies will cause premature needle loss, but deficiencies are not always obvious and trees will utilize available soil K to a much greater extent than required for optimum growth. This phenomenon, known as "luxury consumption", was introduced in section 4.1.1.

The only method to assess K requirements correctly is through foliar analysis, the subject of section 8.2. Soil testing can provide information about initial supplies, but there is not always a good correlation between available soil K and use by plants.

7.1.3 Phosphorus

Trees use only about a 1/10th as much P as N, but it is still an extremely important nutrient. Like K, virtually all of the P available to plants comes from the mineral fraction of the soil or from fertilizer applications.

Areas of good native P supply are apt to be soils derived from geologically young rocks with moderate rainfall in the west and mid-western U.S. Soils formed from marine deposits, especially in the humid Southeastern U.S., tend to have low P content. Lands that have been mowed, grazed or cropped heavily without a conscientious attempt to maintain soil fertility are apt to be P- poor, as are lands that have been subject to erosion.

Unlike N and K, P does not leach very readily from the soil. In fact, P does not move appreciably, and when conditions are very acid or very basic it can become fixed by the soil and unavailable to plants. An exception to this is on some leached, sandy, inert soils, especially in the Southeastern U.S., where P will move readily.

Usually only a very small portion of the total soil P is available to plants at any given time. The balance is either only slowly available or tied up and unavailable until soil chemistry changes. Often, total supplies of P are more than adequate, but its low solubility under all but the most ideal soil conditions can lead to deficiencies. Fortunately, trees—especially the conifers—have adapted to conditions of low P availability.

There are two principal forms of soil P available to plants: $H_2PO_4^-$ and HPO_4^{--}. The former anion is more prevalent under acid conditions (the extra H is a reflection of the fact that more H+ is floating around looking for anions to mate with when conditions are acid), and the latter is more prevalent when conditions are basic. Acid soils tend to bind P as insoluble phosphates of iron (Fe) and aluminum (Al) while basic soil conditions cause the formation of Ca and magnesium (Mg) phosphates that are insoluble as well. Soil pH within the range of 5.5–6.5 is considered optimum to maintain adequate supplies of available P. Of the two forms, plants use H_2PO_4 to a much greater extent than the other form (8, 55).

Phosphorus plays an important role in plant metabolism by helping to mediate energy transfers. It is also involved in photosynthesis, and is a major component of important organic compounds. Adequate supplies of P are associated with a hastening of plant maturity, successful fruiting and good root development (55). Even so, responses to applications of P in conifer plantations are not very common, except in the Southeastern U.S. However, there are instances where a response primarily attributable to N was enhanced by applications of P (14, 22, 40, 46). Occasionally P applications do elicit a response in areas where it is in extremely short supply (1, 22).

Phosphorus nutrition in trees is often a function of the extent to which roots have been infected with mycorrhizae-forming fungi. However, response to P may also be tied to adequate N (22). This effect, along with a discussion of some other significant nutrient interactions, is the subject of section 11.0.

7.1.4 Calcium and Magnesium

Trees use considerable quantities of Ca and Mg, but only about 5% as much of these elements as N. Most soils are capable of supplying adequate quantities of these elements for good tree growth. However, in some coarse-textured soils these nutrients may be lacking, especially when conditions are acidic. Notwithstanding, there are very few examples of conifer responses to applications of these elements.

Calcium nutrition affects many important plant systems: translocation of carbohydrate, protein synthesis, the activity of certain enzyme systems, and ion uptake by roots (55). When Ca supplies are inadequate or blocked from plant use, tissue elongation is affected. In fact, one of the current theories surrounding the debilitating effects of acid rain on forests suggests that Ca deficiencies may be the principal cause of twig die-back in some stands (49).

Magnesium plays a somewhat similar role to Ca with a noteworthy exception—it is the only mineral constituent of chlorophyll serving as the element around which the molecule is formed (55). Deficiencies of Mg can cause "chlorosis" or a bright yellowing of needle tips.

Both Mg and Ca are absorbed by plants as the cations Ca^{++} and Mg^{++}. Supplies of these two ions are usually higher in fine-textured soils, especially those of basic or near-basic reaction. Coarse textured soils with a low cation exchange capacity (shortage of negative charges) are unable to hold many of these ions available to plants. The same situation exists for acidic fine-textured soils where the negatively charged exchange sites are saturated with Al and Fe. Calcium, Mg, and other nutrient cations will leach from the soil under these conditions.

Aside from the important roles these elements play in plant nutrition, oxides of Ca and Mg are the two principal liming agents used to effect an increase in soil pH. Calcium oxide and, to a lesser extent except in some instances where concentrations are higher, Mg oxide are the active ingredients of ground limestone. When these compounds react with an acid soil, free-floating Fe and Al will precipitate as fairly insoluble hydroxides. Calcium and Mg will then occupy the vacant exchange sites on soil particles.

A more detailed discussion of limestone as a fertilizer material is in section 9.6.

7.1.5 Sulfur

Soil supplies of S are usually adequate for most Christmas tree species in most parts of the country. One of the reasons for this is that a major source of supply is the atmosphere which can provide up to 25 pounds of S per acre annually, more in areas affected by industrial emissions (63). Although S exists principally in two soil forms—in organic matter as a constituent of protein, and as the inorganic sulfate (SO_4)—plants absorb the sulfate form. Organic S must be mineralized to sulfate before it can be used by plants. Atmospheric S can be assimilated by leaves, but to good advantage only when concentrations are low. High concentrations of sulfur dioxide (SO_2), a pollutant from the combustion of fossil fuels, can damage leaf tissues.

Sulfur is important in the synthesis of protein, especially the formation of certain amino acids. Some research suggests that adequate S nutrition is essential to efficient nitrogen utilization in Douglas-fir in the Northwestern U.S. (56). As foliar N levels increase, S levels should be increased. In plantations where S is lacking, trees may not respond to N applications even though N is lacking. Since both elements are important constituents of protein, it is not surprising to see such a strong interaction. Deficiencies of S result in yellowing-symptoms similar to N deficiencies, with an important exception. Because S is not very mobile in the plant, yellowing first appears in younger tissue. N deficiencies usually first show up on older leaves because the demands of younger tissue cause it to be exported.

Sulfur is commonly applied in situations where soil pH needs to be lowered. Its use as an acidifying agent is discussed further in section 9.6.

7.2 Micronutrients

As the name of this class of nutrients implies, plant requirements for the remaining 7 essential nutrients are considerably less than for those already discussed. Also known as "trace" elements, Christmas tree crops may require as little as a few ounces of these elements per acre. However, the absence of one or more of the micronutrients can cause problems for the grower. Fortunately, micronutrient deficiencies are rare in Christmas tree culture, more often caused by careless use of fertilizers, than to a lack of supplies in the soil. Ironically, many commercially available N-P-K fertilizers contain trace elements as impurities.

Since micronutrients are used by plants in such very small quantities, not as much is known about their role in plant nutrition as is known about macronutrients. Plant requirements are so small as to make it difficult to design experiments that eliminate these elements. Most of what is known comes from studies that have evolved from the correction of diagnosed deficiencies in agronomic crops.

The availability of micronutrients will decrease as soil pH increases. This is true for boron (B), copper (Cu), iron (Fe), manganese (Mn) and zinc (Zn). When soil pH is kept within the range of 5.0–6.0, which is favorable for most of the conifers, adequate availability of these elements is usually not a problem. However, application of excessive amounts of lime to raise soil pH to within this range may cause temporary deficiencies of one or more of these elements. The availability of molybdenum (Mo), used by plants in extremely small quantities, increases as soil pH increases. Not much is known about chlorine (Cl).

Since micronutrients are used by trees in such small quantities, the range between deficiency and toxicity is often very narrow. It is important for this reason not to apply these elements indiscriminately. However, as was mentioned earlier, micronutrient deficiencies are often the result of unfavorable soil chemistry. Application of micronutrients under these circumstances will usually have no effect because they will become locked-up in the soil. Foliar applications of specially formulated solutions are much more effective until soil chemistry can be corrected.

A discussion of the use of micronutrient preparations is included in section 9.5.

8.0 ANALYZING THE NUTRIENT STATUS OF THE PLANTATION

Just as it is impossible for a physician to prescribe a pharmaceutical without a thorough examination of the patient, so too it is impossible for the Christmas tree grower to use fertilizers to good effect without information on the current nutrient status of the plantation. Soil testing and foliar analysis are two common means of assessing fertility. The objective of these analyses is to identify nutrient imbalances, suggest guidelines for treating them, and to provide baseline information on natural site fertility and changes resulting from fertilization.

Both soil testing and foliar analysis involve gathering samples that are representative of the general conditions of the plantation. For this reason, it is absolutely essential that the grower gather samples according to the procedures suggested by the lab that will do the analysis, or according to the methods outlined here. The most common error in fertility analysis is failure to gather a representative sample. Most often, the sampling area is too large, and conditions within the plantation too variable, to allow a meaningful analysis of fertility. This section will discuss some of the assumptions on which testing is based, sources of sample variation, and how the grower can partition variability in the plantation.

8.1 Soil Testing

Once a grower has decided to establish a plantation in an area, one of the first tasks—even before trees are ordered—is to have the soil tested. This is best done six months to a year before planting, in late summer or early fall when soil nutrient concentrations are most stable. Why so far in advance? Because if the site requires amendments they can be applied and given ample time to react with the soil before the trees arrive. This is especially true for limestone applications. Since most people sample soils in the spring to prepare for the growing season, swamping the labs with samples and causing delays, fall sampling is much preferred.

Soil characteristics can vary tremendously over short

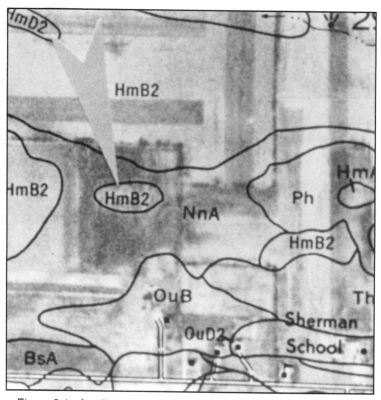

Figure 8-1. A soil survey map showing different soil types identified and delineated on an aerial photograph. The characteristics of types are found in a key that accompanies the map. With permission of the Soil Convservation Service.

distances. For this reason, the grower must delineate areas that differ due to drainage and slope, or to obvious differences in soil texture and color. This is not always easy. One of the best sources of information on soil types is the USDA Soil Conservation Service (SCS). With offices located in virtually every county across the country, SCS soil survey maps can help identify potential sources of variation in the plantation even before soil samples are gathered (Figure 8-1). In addition to map information, the soil survey also provides useful descriptions of soil characteristics and limitations for specific uses. Often this information includes statements about the natural fertility of soils.

Not every county has a recent soil survey, but the chances of information being available are good in counties that have a lot of agricultural production.

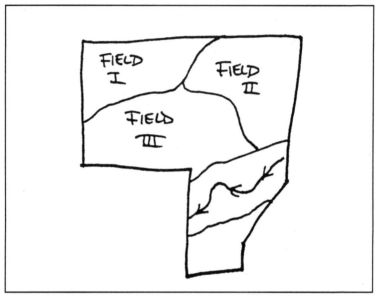

Figure 8-2. The plantation divided into 3 sampling units on the basis of soil type and drainage.

Major changes in soil types should be identified and established as sampling units (Figure 8-2). Each sampling unit is treated independently. Within a sampling unit, a single soil sample that is representative of the area is gathered in the following fashion.

Using a clean plastic pail and a spade, the grower should walk across the entire sampling unit, stopping 12–16 times at random to obtain a sub-sample of soil (Figure 8-3). The soil is gathered from the flat side of a spade-cut to a depth of 4 to 6 inches. At each sample hole, the grower should gather a hand- full of soil by drawing the fingers along the spade-cut from the bottom to the top of the hole. After all the sub-samples have been gathered from a single unit, the soil in the

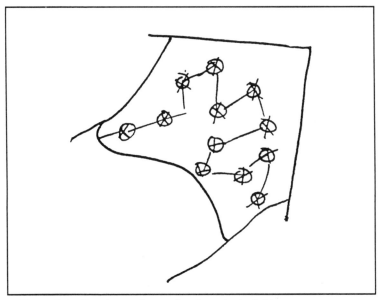

Figure 8-3. Random soil sampling in a single field.

bucket should be thoroughly mixed and a single sample extracted for lab analyses. The sample should include about a pint of soil.

There are special tools available for extracting soil cores that ensure uniformity of sub-samples both in terms of their total volume and amount of soil taken at each depth (Figure 8-4).

The need for partitioning an area into relatively homogeneous sampling units, and for randomness in the selection of sites where soil is to be gathered are tied to the following statistics. If a sampling unit is one acre in size, there are about 2,000,000 lbs. of soil that could be sampled. Twelve soil sub-samples gathered at random then mixed, with one composite sample sent to the lab, represents a sample of "sub-samples" from less than 0.00015% of the soil in the unit. If the unit were perfectly homogeneous, this would be more than enough to discover site fertility. However, soils are not very homogeneous so the grower must ensure potential sources of variation are kept to a minimum.

47

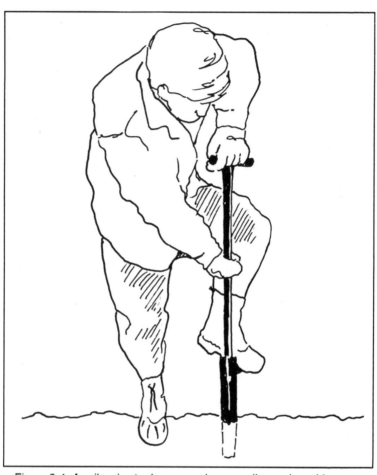

Figure 8-4. A soil coring tool can speed up sampling and provide more uniform samples.

All future soil samples should be gathered at approximately the same time of year as the first sample was gathered. Seasonal variations in nutrient concentrations can make interpretation of fertility trends very difficult if samples are taken at different times of year.

8.1.1 Interpreting Soil Test Results

There is no standard lab analysis for soil and every lab

uses slightly different analytical procedures and methods of reporting the results. Unfortunately, the same soil analyzed in two different labs may appear to have come from very different sites. Since soil test results are rarely comparable between labs, growers should make a carefully informed decision about which lab to use initially and stick to that decision for at least a tree rotation. The grower must also remember that soil analysis provides an index of fertility, not absolute values. Fortunately, most labs are consistent so that changes in fertility over time should be apparent. Switching labs midway through the rotation, in effect, changes the scale on which the index is based making comparison of trends extremely difficult.

Labs usually offer a standard package that includes three or four elements, plus soil pH and some measure of how much lime is needed to change pH. The most common elements are K, P, Mg and N. Soil N is seasonally variable and crops are usually supplemented with fertilizer N regardless of reserves, so many labs do not test for it. Also, as a practical matter, soil tests for N have not been very useful as an index of N availability. Other elements and analyses can usually be added to the standard package.

Test values may be reported in percent, parts per million (ppm), parts per two million (pp2m) and/or pounds per acre. Since there are about 2,000,000 lbs. of soil in the top 6–8 inches of an "average" soil, pp2m can be used directly as pounds per acre. Some labs will report soil test values as high, medium or

```
 1000    01/23/91   CHITTENDEN       COMMERCIAL SOIL TEST RECOMMENDATIONS
lab no.    date      county          University of Vermont - Agricultural Testing Lab

             SOIL TEST RESULTS         LOW    MEDIUM    HIGH    VERY HIGH
                      (lbs/acre)
Available phosphate (P205)      3      **********
Reserve phosphate (P205)      175      **********
Potash (K20)                  120      *******************
Magnesium (Mg)                 45      **********
Aluminum (Al)                 285      ****************************************
pH                            5.0      **********

Lime requirement (target pH = 6.0)   4.5 tons/acre
             REPORT FOR                                      FIELD TWO

        Jim Smith
        RD                              RECOMMENDATIONS FOR
        Richmond, VT   05477
                                          Xmas trees - balsam fir
```

Figure 8-5. A University testing lab soil report.

low (Figure 8-5). This is a relative indicator of fertility, usually for crop plants, that tells farmers something about the degree to which a crop will respond to an element. A "low" value suggests the possibility of a large response to applications of the element. A "high" value suggests that no response will be obtained. Unless otherwise indicated, these values are not applicable to Christmas trees.

Soil test values should never be treated as absolute numbers. In other words, when the report shows there are 80 pounds per acre of potassium oxide, do not assume a fertilizer application that provides 40 pounds of potassium oxide will bring the total to 120 pounds per acre. Soils are much too complex to allow such simple arithmetic.

An interpretation of soil test results for Christmas trees is not as easy as it is for crops. The purpose of interpretation is to develop recommendations that will optimize yield. For most crops, soil interpretations and fertilizer recommendations are based on yield-response research. These studies try to predict how crop yield will change when a given soil is supplemented with fertilizers. Response data do not exist for Christmas trees across a range of soil conditions, so interpretation is on a case-by-case basis. Fertilizer recommendations are usually given as general guidelines, and response is often uncertain. Fortunately, there are some published minimum soil test values for conifers (42). These values are listed in Table 8-1.

TABLE 8-1 Minimum soil fertility levels for growth of conifers on mostly sandy glacial forest soils stocked with pine and spruce. Summarized from Morrison, 1974 (42).

	Lbs./acre (Range)	Lbs./acre (Average)
Available phosphate	4–39	22
Exchangeable magnesium oxide	29–160	66
Available potassium oxide	50–125	84
Available calcium oxide	200–1200	580
Total nitrogen	840–2400	1650

An example of a soil test report from a university soil testing lab is shown in Figure 8-5. The test results are for a soil gathered from an abandoned pasture in the Northeast U.S. It is a sandy loam and will be planted to balsam fir Christmas trees.

An interpretation of the results reported for the sample in Figure 8-5 is as follows:

Available phosphate (P_2O_5)

This is the portion of P that is readily available to trees, and in this instance available-P is low. Values of 10 or above are adequate for plantation establishment, but an acceptable target range for available-P is 15–30 lbs. per acre. Often, fertilizer P is applied at the time of planting to supplement available P. Special care must be used to ensure that fertilizer is not locked up in the reserve pool.

Reserve phosphate (P_2O_5)

This is the portion of P that is not readily available. Reserve- P is locked-up in the mineral fraction of the soil and generally not available. However, as soil chemistry changes (an increase in the pH of an acid soil) and as available sources of P are used up, reserve sources become more available. The rate at which this occurs is very slow, but probably more than adequate for most Christmas tree species.

Some fine-textured, acidic agricultural soils may have extremely high levels of reserve-P, sometimes more than 300 lbs. per acre. Broadcast application of phosphate to an acid soil will increase reserve-P levels. However, the more strongly acid the soil, the more tightly held and less available-P becomes. Abandoned crop lands that have been fertilized intensively will usually show very high reserve-P levels. A target range for reserve-P in most instances is 30–100 lbs. per acre, except in sandy soils where lower values expected.

Potash (K_2O)

Potassium oxide levels in Figure 8-5 are presently adequate for Christmas trees. Soil test values should be kept within the range of 100–150 lbs. per acre until K utilization can be verified with foliar analysis. Some clay and clay loam soils (not suitable for balsam fir) may have potassium oxide levels that are four or five times the values shown here.

Magnesium

Elemental Mg levels are very low. Soil test values should fall within the range of 150–250 lbs. per acre, although excessively sandy soils may not be able to hold this much Mg. Tree demands for Mg are usually low but the presence of Mg will improve soil chemistry, especially when soils are acid. As with K, Mg utilization needs to be verified with foliar analysis. When Mg values are low, the soil is usually fairly acid. Application of agricultural limestone to raise pH may also supplement Mg levels, since Mg is commonly found in many limestone deposits. If limestone sources are not enough, or Mg needs to be supplied without altering pH, other sources are available. (see section 9.4).

Aluminum

Aluminum is not an essential nutrient but it does have a substantial effect on soil chemistry. In Figure 8-5, Al is given as an indication of the amount of acid in the soil. Aluminum reacts with lime to form insoluble aluminum-hydroxy compounds. The more Al ions in the soil, the more lime required to react with it before pH can increase. Iron is a lime-consuming culprit is some parts of the country. However, since labs vary their procedures in figuring the effects of Al and Fe on acid amount, the grower should specify a target pH at which lime requirement for the sample is to be calculated.

pH

Soil pH is one of the most important and useful measures of the soil test. Its significance is discussed in section 5.3. Soil testing labs use one of two different procedures to measure pH. Some use a salt solution of potassium or calcium chloride to overcome the effect that soil salts have on pH readings, while others use a suspension of soil and distilled water. Salt-pH values are usually about one-half to one unit lower than the pH of soil in water. In Figure 8-5, pH is determined with the soil-in-water method.

Scientists who study forest soils argue that the soil-in-water pH method is more meaningful for trees. The agronomists say that the effects of salts in crop soils must be overcome to get a true measure of soil pH. It makes little difference which method is used so long as the grower

Texture of 7-inch (18 cm.) Plow Layer	ph Range			
	4.5 to 4.9	5.0 to 5.4	5.5 to 5.9	6.0 to 6.4
	... (tons of lime recommended per acre [1])			
Sands	2-1/2	2-1/2	1/2[2]	
Loamy sands	3	2-1/2	2	1
Sandy loans	4	3	2-1/2	1-1/2
Clay loams and loams	5	4	3	2
Clays and silty clays	6	5	4	2

[1] Lime recommendations based on a ground limestone material having a neutralizing value of 90 percent with 100 percent of it passing through a 20-mesh (850-micron) sieve and 75 percent passing through a 100-mesh (150-micron) sieve.

[2] It is preferable to recommend a minimum of 1 ton per acre (2.24 mt/ha) so as to obtain uniform application and to justify the expense of application.

Notes:
1. For each inch of depth of plowing below 7 inches (18 cm.), increase the rate of lime applied by 15 percent.
2. To convert from tons per acre to metric tons per hectare, multiply by 2.24.
3. For each 1 percent increase in soil organic matter above 5 percent, reduce the rate of lime by 1/2 ton per acre. This seems to be a contradiction because humus buffers the soil; however, the more the humus the lower the pH requirement of plants.

TABLE 2 Approximate Tons of Agricultural Limestone Required to Raise the pH of the 7 inch Plow Layer of Five Contrasting Soil Textural Classes with 5 Percent Organic Matter Under Four pH Ranges. From: "Our Soils and Their Management," 6th Ed., 1990. Used with permission of Interstate Publishers.

knows. Most soil testing labs use the soil-in-water method although it is not always clearly indicated which method has been used.

A pH by the soil-in-water method of 5.0 is low for most Christmas tree species, but near optimum for some like Scots pine. To change the pH, up or down, we need to know something about how much acidity there is, since pH is only a measure of acid intensity. An acceptable target range for most Christmas tree species is a soil-in-water pH of 5.0–6.0. The pH preferences of different species are discussed in section 12.0.

There are different indices of acid amount in a soil, the simplest is soil texture. Fine textured, clay soils have many times more acid to neutralize at a given pH that do coarse, sandy soils. Home-use pH tester kits that rely on indicator dyes will often use soil texture as an index of buffer capacity. The purpose of estimating acid amount is to figure how much lime must be applied to raise the pH to a certain "target" level. This value is often reported in the soil test results as the "lime requirement".

Lime Requirement

To raise the pH of the test soil from 5.0 to 6.0, the grower needs to apply 4.5 tons of agricultural lime per acre. Lime requirement takes into account not only the pH of the soil, but also the acid amount. Soils with high levels of Al and Fe will have higher lime requirements at a given pH than soils where Al and Fe levels are lower. Note, however, that 4.5 tons per acre is a very high rate, more than twice the amount that should be applied at any one time. Placement and timing of limestone applications is the subject of section 10.4.

The lime requirement of a soil is always given for a specified target pH. If it is to be used directly from the soil test report, growers need to be sure that the specified target pH is within an acceptable range for the plantation in question.

Lime requirement can also be estimated on the basis of soil texture, as in Table 8-2. Soil pH tester kits commonly use lime requirement tables based on soil texture, although the table method is not nearly as accurate as a measurement based on soil chemistry.

Summary

Often labs will offer fertilizer recommendations if a crop has been specified. Unfortunately, Christmas trees are not usually recognized as a crop, and if they are, the recommendations are apt to be very general and on a per-acre basis. Since most growers fertilize individual trees or rows of trees, recommendations given in pounds per acre will need to be converted to ounces per tree. Appendix B lists some useful conversions.

Home-use soil testing kits are available but they cannot offer the same accuracy as a lab analysis and are quite expensive. The best value in kits is one that tests only soil pH. Growers who use these kits should follow the directions very carefully, using the same methods outlined here to obtain samples. Also, it takes a well-trained and experienced eye to interpret the color change of indicator dyes used with these kits. A poor reading can result in error.

After the initial soil test has been completed and the recommendations followed, future soil tests must take into account the methods used to adjust fertility on the site. When individual trees or rows of trees are fertilized, soil tests gathered between rows will not accurately reflect the conditions in the rooting zone. Soil samples must be gathered from treated areas. However, the chances of picking up even a single grain of fertilizer that could ruin a sample are much greater from soils gathered around the base of trees. For this reason, soil sampling should take place in the fall after fertilizers have had a chance to react with the soil. Once the plantation is well established the grower should switch to foliar analysis, using the concentration of nutrients in foliage as an indicator of site fertility. However, soil pH will still need to be monitored with periodic sampling of the upper 3 or 4 inches of soil.

Under most circumstances, two or three soil tests during a rotation are adequate. The first, as much as a year before the new plantation is established; the second test, midway through the rotation, and a third test taken about a year or two before the end of the rotation to help plan the fertility program for the next plantation.

8.2 Foliar Analysis

Foliar analysis provides a measure of the concentration of nutrients in current-year needles. It is an excellent indicator of relative site fertility and the degree to which trees are capable of using nutrients from the soil. Since leaves are a primary metabolic center, changes in nutrient supplies are quickly reflected in the leaves (33). Also, foliar nutrient content is tied to the performance of the whole tree. When tree needles have adequate nutrition, the rest of the plant is usually in good shape.

Unfortunately, foliar analysis is not a very well developed diagnostic procedure for Christmas trees so interpretations and fertilizer recommendations for some species are not always easy to make. Foliar nutrient concentrations for some commercially important Christmas tree species are listed in Table 8-3.

TABLE 8-3 Expected range of nutrient concentrations in percent of oven-dry weight for conifer foliage. Adapted from Morrison, (1974), except values for balsam fir that were adapted from Krause and Hamilton (1981), and values for Douglas fir adapted from Van den Driessche (1979).

Species	Deficient	% O.D. Wt.	Adequate
		Nitrogen	
Norway spruce	1.30		1.80
White spruce	1.30		1.50
Red pine	1.30		1.80
Scots pine	1.00		1.50
Balsam fir	1.30		1.80
Douglas fir	1.20		1.80
		Phosphorus	
Norway spruce	0.15		0.20
White spruce	0.14		0.18
Red pine	0.12		0.15
Scots pine	0.14		0.17
Balsam fir	0.11		0.18
Douglas fir	0.14		0.22
		Potassium	
Norway spruce	0.30		0.45
White spruce	0.24		0.44
Red pine	—		0.45
White pine	—		0.45
Scots pine	0.45		0.60
Balsam fir	0.26		0.65
Douglas fir	0.40		0.80
		Calcium	
Norway spruce	0.10		0.12
White spruce	0.10		0.15
Red pine	0.03		0.04
Douglas fir	—		0.20
		Magnesium	
Norway spruce	0.10		0.12
White spruce	0.06		0.10
Red pine	0.05		0.07
Balsam fir	0.05		0.11
Douglas fir	—		0.12

The field procedure to obtain foliage for analysis is similar to soil sampling. Foliage must be gathered from trees that represent the average conditions for the plantation, or for a group of trees in question. Whole, undamaged, first-year needles from the top of the tree are gathered in the fall, just after the onset of dormancy. Research has shown that nutrient content is highest and most stable at this time of year. Virtually all of the guidelines and indicators of foliar nutrient status are based on fall sampling of foliage near the top of the tree. It is extremely important that growers adhere to this sampling procedure to obtain comparable results.

The lab will need at least two ounces of fresh needles. If there is a delay between the time needles are gathered and delivered to the lab, the sample should be refrigerated, but for no more than a few days. Growers should follow the sample size and handling directions supplied by the lab.

The analysis can include as many nutrients as the grower requires. However, if more than six elements are to be determined, the foliage sample may need to be larger. Nitrogen, P, K, Mg, S, and Ca are the elements most commonly analyzed. Test values are reported as parts per million (ppm), or as a percentage of the sample's weight (1.0% is equal to 10,000 ppm). To allow comparison of the results with the table values listed in Table 8-3, growers should specify that the results be reported on a dry-weight basis.

8.2.1 Interpreting the Foliar Analysis Results

There are very few specific guidelines for interpreting the foliar nutrient status of Christmas trees. Notwithstanding, a number of studies with conifers have been completed so there is sufficient information to allow some interpretation, but not necessarily for those qualities a Christmas tree grower is trying to obtain, such as dark green color. Developing a prescription to supplement fertility or correct a deficiency is mostly a matter or trial and error. It is up to the grower to develop guidelines.

Growers may assume that if test values approximate those listed in Table 8-3, nutrition is adequate. However, most comparisons will disclose an imbalance of one or more nutrients. In Section 4.3, a theory of plant nutrition known as "nutrient balancing" is discussed. The premise of this theory is that the relative proportions of nutrients in the plant are more important to growth and development than absolute amounts. When the proportions are balanced, increases in growth rate are a function of nutrient supply up to the biological capacity of the tree. When proportions are unbalanced, increasing nutrient supplies will not increase growth, and may suppress it. Table 8-4 shows foliar nutrient standards for balsam fir using the nutrient balancing concept. Notice that nutrient status is a function of an element's concentration in the plant relative to N.

Nutrient Status	N%	P%/N%	K%/N%	MG%/N%
Severely deficient	< 1.3	< 0.08	< 0.20	< 0.04
Moderately deficient	1.3 -1.59	0.08 - 0.089	0.20 - 0.29	0.04 - 0.05
Critical	1.6 -1.69	0.09 - 0.10	0.30 - 0.35	0.051- 0.06
Adequate	1.7-2.0	> 0.10	> 0.35	> 0.06
Excessive	> 2.00`	—	—	—

TABLE 8-4. Provisional foliar nutrient standards for balsam fir Christmas tree culture, according to Krause and Hamilton (1981). Values for nitrogen are percent of oven-dry weight. Other values are the ratios of percent oven-dry weight of the element in question to the percent oven-dry weight of nitrogen.

The balance, or ratio of one essential nutrient to another, is believed to be similar for almost all green plants. Ingestad (24) suggests the following ratio of foliar nutrient concentrations: N-100:P-15:K-50:Ca-5:Mg-5. In other words, an optimum nutrient balance for a green plant is obtained when P concentration is 15% of N, K is 50% of N, and Ca and Mg are 5% of N. When this ratio exists, growth rate will increase in proportion to N levels up to a biological optimum. For most conifer species, optimum foliar N levels are 1.5–2.0%. Ingestad (26) suggests slight variations in the ratios for different species groups. For example, pine requires slightly lower concentrations of P and K than does spruce. He also suggests that water-use efficiency and winter hardiness can be improved by slightly increasing the proportion of K, especially with species that have low K uptake efficiency. Important secondary- and micronutrient proportions, are listed in Table 8-5.

TABLE 8-5 Nutrient adequacy for secondary and micronutrients expressed as a percentage of their oven-dry weights to that of nitrogen. For example, adequate S is 0.09 times that of N. When N concentration is 1.8%, adequate S is 0.162%. Adapted from Ingestad (26).

Nutrient	$\dfrac{\text{nutrient } \%}{\text{Nitrogen } \%}$ X 100
Sulfur	9.0
Iron	0.7
Manganese	0.4
Boron	0.2
Copper	0.03
Zinc	0.03
Chlorine	0.03
Molybdenum	0.007
Sodium	0.003

Since foliar analysis is commonly used as a diagnostic procedure to spot deficiencies and imbalances, fertilizer recommendations are rarely given with the test results. Growers should learn to develop their own guidelines based upon careful recordkeeping. Rates of application of various fertilizers are discussed in Section 13.0.

Aside from its use to help spot nutrient deficiencies, foliar analysis does not usually need to be done any more frequently than twice during a rotation. Midway through a rotation it is good tool to avert deficiencies or imbalances; and in the year preceding harvest, to tailor fertilizer applications so trees have good color and a healthy appearance when they go to market.

A final word about testing labs is in order. There are hundreds of labs around the country. Although most adhere to a set of standards agreed upon by chemists, some labs are better and more reliable than others. Prices and capabilities differ too. Growers who have no prior experience with agricultural testing labs should seek advice from other local growers. In general, a local lab will provide a more useful and tailored analysis than an out-of-state lab. Also, most state universities have testing labs that will do soil and foliar analyses. The county Cooperative Extension Agent can provide information on testing facilities at the state university.

Growers should also bear in mind that there is virtually no correlation between soil test results and foliar analysis. Therefore, the two should be viewed as separate indices of plantation fertility.

8.3 Recognizing Nutrient Deficiencies

Obvious nutrient deficiencies in forest trees growing under natural conditions are very rare. When soils are poor, trees establish an equilibrium with the site such that their capacity for growth is tied directly to nutrient availability. Trees that are in balance with a poor site, though growing slower, may look similar to trees growing on a fertile site. In Christmas tree plantations, nutrient deficiencies that cause poor color and other problems are most often caused by imbalances; when the supply of one element or group of elements increases while the others remain constant.

Technically, a deficiency implies that trees will "respond" to an application of an element that is lacking. The degree of response is a function of the severity of the deficiency. Unfortunately, deficiencies are not always obvious, and when they are, substantial growth losses or damage may have already occurred. Minor deficiencies can happen without apparent symptoms. This condition is known as "hidden hunger" and it is impossible to detect without foliar analysis.

The most common visual symptom of a nutrient deficiency is foliage yellowing. Also known as "chlorosis", deficiencies of N, K, Mg, Ca, S, Fe and Mn will cause foliage to turn yellow. However, knowing which leaves turn yellow will narrow the field of elements that might be causing the problem.

Some elements are mobile within the plant. When there is a shortage, supplies of a mobile element are moved from older leaves to younger, causing symptoms of deficiency first in older leaves. Conversely, immobile elements tend to exhibit deficiencies first on new leaves. Table 8-6 lists the relative mobility for some of the essential elements.

TABLE 8-6. The relative mobility of nutrients in plant tissues.

Mobile (symptoms on older tissue)	Immobile (symptoms on younger tissue)
Nitrogen	Calcium
Phosphorus	Sulfur
Potassium	Iron
Magnesium	Manganese
	Zinc

Yellowing is also caused by non-nutrient related factors, such as wet soils and disease, but it could be natural at certain times of the year in some species. Other deficiency symptoms include needle twisting and fusing, premature needle drop, resin exudation (also caused by insects), and—in severe cases of deficiency—twisting, crooking and dieback of shoots.

Specific deficiency symptoms for some of the elements are:

Nitrogen—General yellowing of older needles. Severely deficient trees may exhibit stunted needles. Moderate deficiencies of N are very common in most Christmas tree plantations.

Phosphorus—While young needles are green or slightly yellow-green, older needles may be tinged with purple. Phosphorus deficiencies are difficult to detect without foliar analysis.

Potassium—Symptoms may be similar to those caused by N deficiency. Needle stunting may be more apparent. A yellowing of shoot tips and needle shedding may occur in the fall.

Magnesium—A bright yellowing of needle tips is very characteristic of Mg deficiency.

Sulfur—Symptoms are similar to N except they show first on younger tissue.

Calcium—A general yellowing, similar to N deficiency except more apparent on younger needles. Severe deficiencies can cause shoots to die back.

Manganese and iron—Yellowing of new foliage.

The best method of identifying nutrient deficiencies before they cause visual symptoms is foliar analysis. However, since one of the most common causes of deficiencies in the Christmas tree plantation is careless use of fertilizers, deficiencies can be prevented by carefully tailoring the fertility program to the capabilities of the site and the needs of the trees. An excess of one element can cause a deficiency in another even when adequate supplies are present. This is known as antagonism and will be discussed further in section 11.0.

8.4 Measuring Fertilizer Response and Recordkeeping

The validity of soil testing and foliar analysis is based on the premise that plant growth and yield are predictable functions of site fertility, and that poor soils, or soils lacking in a particular element, can be fertilized to improve yield at different levels of efficiency. For example, the results of a soil test might suggest that one unit of element X will increase growth rate by 50%, but two units of X will increase growth by 65%. The grower is posed with the question, "Is the extra cost of another unit of fertilizer worth only 15% more growth?."

Knowing how crops will react to applications of nutrients that are in short supply is the product of many years of research. Unfortunately, there is very little information on predicting the response of Christmas trees to fertilizers. Therefore, the grower must learn to measure response and apply fertilizers according to needs.

Of the five cultural characteristics of Christmas trees, discussed in section 2.0, that a Christmas tree grower wants to improve, two—foliage color and density—are easily assessed as indicators of fertilizer response. A grower who carefully monitors the effects of fertilizer treatments on these two factors will, in time, be able to answer the questions, "Is the application of another unit of fertilizer worth the expense?"; or, "Can I obtain a similar response with only half as much?."

Accurately monitoring fertilizer response requires three things, 1) a system to measure the factors consistently and objectively, 2) a method to test the effects of different fertilizer formulations and amounts and, 3) carefully maintained records. The methods suggested here are considerably less involved than would be employed to scientifically test hypotheses about fertilizer response. However, the foundation of any inquiry, informal or otherwise, is careful observation and notation.

The effects of treatments on closely monitored trees in the plantation, called sample trees, will provide an observant grower with useful information about fertilizer response that is applicable to the entire plantation.

Sample trees should be randomly selected individuals that are in good health and representative of the general condition of trees in the plantation. This can be accomplished by devising an easy system to identify all trees in the plantation. For example, by assigning rows , and trees within rows, identifying numbers, a randomly selected subset of the entire plantation can be quickly established. Each randomly selected tree is visited to make sure that it is a good representative of other trees in the plantation, then the tree is marked with flagging tape and its "address" in the plantation noted. A nearby tree with similar characteristics can be selected and marked as well. This neighbor may be useful for a "paired comparison" of response to test more than one treatment at a time. Also, if the sample tree dies or is harvested, the paired individual can take its place provided it has been treated similarly. The more trees selected for monitoring, the better. However, 20–30 trees should suffice. These trees should be scattered throughout the plantation. After sample trees have been selected, foliage color and density is assessed and recorded. These assessments should take place in the fall, after the onset of dormancy.

Foliage color is assessed by comparing the color of needles to some standard, usually a plant tissue color chart. The color chart offers a range of hues between yellow-green and blue-green, allowing the grower to pick the color chip that best matches foliage. Even minor changes in foliage color are easily detected and recorded using the color chart. However, the hue of a color is affected by light, so light conditions during sampling must approximate the conditions of earlier sampling periods. To eliminate this effect, foliage samples should be illuminated with an artificial light source. Since this may be impractical in the field, needle samples can be gathered and compared to color charts in the office. These same needles, or a subset of them, may also be used for foliar analysis.

Growers and researchers have had mixed feelings about the validity of color charts. Some argue that the range of hues does not adequately approximate foliage colors. Unfortunately, there are no standard charts for Christmas trees, and only one chart on foliage that is commercially available in the U.S. from the Munsell Color Division. Another source of color charts, described by some researchers as more suitable for use with Christmas tree foliage is the Royal Horticultural Society Colour Charts. Addresses for both of these sources are listed in Appendix D. A grower may also want to consider constructing a chart for the plantation using color chips available at most paint stores. However, without using an established standard like the Munsell charts or the R.H.S. Colour Charts as a basis for comparison, a grower-constructed chart will have little application outside of the plantation for which it was developed. Since the objective of the grower who uses color charts is to observe trends, estimate the degree to which foliage colors have changed, and correlate changes with fertilizer applications, just about any system that can monitor color changes will suffice. Even color print photography should work well.

Foliage density can be assessed in two ways: 1) counting

the number of resting buds on each of three or four lateral branches near the top of the crown, then averaging to obtain number of buds per lateral; and 2) measuring needle length. Fertility influences bud formation and needle length, both of which determine foliage density and, indirectly, tree value. Although an estimate of the number of buds per lateral is best determined in the field, needle lengths can be obtained in the office from the foliage gathered for color and nutrient analysis.

The purpose of recording foliage color and density is to establish a relationship between these factors and the nutrient status of the plantation as determined by soil and foliar analysis. When nutrient conditions are less than optimum, fertilizer applications should have a positive effect on foliage color and density. Selected sample trees, or nearby trees that are "paired" to the sample trees, can be used to assess the effects of different treatments. However, the more treatments a grower tries, the more complicated things become and the more difficult it is to interpret results. Also, trees are quite variable so it is difficult to detect a uniform effect from fertilizer treatments.

There is no point in using fertilizers if the trees do not respond in some positive way that translates into cost savings and/or higher value. However, since trees do not always respond to fertilizers in the current year, it is hard for the grower to assess the value of treatments without good records. Fertilizer application rates, formulations, costs, dates and special notes about conditions in the plantation are important to note. For instance, an early spring nitrogen application followed by 5 days of heavy rain will probably supply very little N to the trees. Failure to note the impact of this event on N supplies may cause the grower to double rates in future years.

A journal of water-proof paper and pencil is used to record data from sample trees. Always record the date of measurements and any notes that will help maintain consistency of the measurements and recording in the future. After studying the data from sample trees, the grower should write down an interpretation of the results and develop a fertilizer prescription for the coming year. By comparing this prescription with those of past years, obvious trends may emerge and the current year can be modified accordingly.

Careful observations and good records are essential to the grower who is striving to develop a cost efficient and effective fertility program.

9.0 FERTILIZER MATERIALS

Thanks to American agriculture, there are dozens of different fertilizers available to Christmas tree growers. Blends of these materials offer an almost infinite range of ratios of one element to another and a variety of different physical characteristics. However, not all are suitable for Christmas trees, and some may be more cost-effective than others in certain regions.

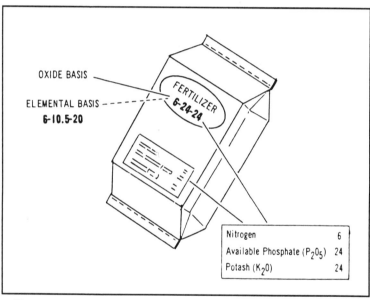

OXIDE BASIS

ELEMENTAL BASIS
6-10.5-20

FERTILIZER
6-24-24

Nitrogen	6
Available Phosphate (P_2O_5)	24
Potash (K_2O)	24

Figure 9-1. The guaranteed analysis or grade shows the percentage of elemental nitrogen and the oxides of P and K. Used with permission of Interstate Publishers.

The purpose of this section is to describe common fertilizers used with Christmas trees and how these materials are identified and sold. Also discussed are the effects of different fertilizer sources of an element on tree growth, and placement and timing considerations. Fertilizer blending and costs are discussed as well.

Strictly speaking, a "fertilizer material" is a single com-

oxides	Converting to elements	multiply by	elements	Converting to oxides	multiply by
P₂O₅	P	0.436	P	P₂O₅	2.291
K₂O	K	0.830	K	K₂O	1.205
CaO	Ca	0.715	Ca	CaO	1.399
CaCO₃	Ca	0.400	Ca	CaCO₃	2.497
Mg O	Mg	0.603	Mg	MgO	1.658
CaCO₃	CaO	0.560	CaO	CaCO₃	1.785

TABLE 9-1. Oxide equivalents for Some Common Elements.

pound that provides at least one, but no more than two elements. A "mixed fertilizer" is a blend of two or more fertilizer materials which provide two or more essential elements. The nutrient content of fertilizers, whether a single compound or a mix, is always specified on the bag or container (Figure 9-1). Called the "guaranteed analysis" or "grade", it is a set of three numbers. The first is the percentage of elemental nitrogen (N), the second number is percentage phosphate (P_2O_5), and the third is percentage potassium oxide or potash (K_2O). Note the difference in these numbers. Only N is reported in is elemental form, while P and K are reported as oxides. This is an extremely unfortunate convention, particularly since oxides of P and K are not known to exist in soils or plants.

A guaranteed analysis of 5-10-10 indicates that 5% of the material by weight is N, 10% P_2O_5 and 10% K_2O. Conversion factors to determine the elemental content of oxides are found in Table 9-1. A hundred pounds of 5-10-10 will provide 5 lbs. of N, but only about 4.4 lbs. of elemental P and 8.3 lbs. of K. Since fertilizer recommendations are commonly given in both pounds of element required per acre or pounds of a given fertilizer that should be applied, growers need to pay particular attention to the units. The guaranteed analysis also specifies the fertilizer materials, or compounds, that serve as the sources of nutrients. Knowing which sources are best is almost as important as grade in selecting a fertilizer.

9.1 Nitrogen Sources

Of the essential nutrients, N is the only one that is mostly obtained from the atmosphere. Using natural gas as a source of both energy and hydrogen, atmospheric N is combined with H to form ammonia (NH_3). Although small amounts of N are obtained from animal by-products, most fertilizer N is an inorganic reaction product of ammonia and other elements.

Some of the common N sources are listed in Table 9-2, along with fertilizer sources of other primary and some secondary nutrients.

Sources of N that have at least a portion supplied by ammonium (NH_4) are preferred for growing conifers over nitrate (NO_3) sources. Trees will use N supplied by nitrate but they seem to respond better when NH_4 is present as well. Urea, a very commonly used and concentrated source of N will break down into NH_4. However, since the nitrate is lacking, nutrition studies in conifers consistently demonstrate that ammonium nitrate is a better source of N, even though urea may be cheaper.

9.1.1 Ammonium Nitrogen

Ammonium nitrate (AN) is a salt of the ammonium cation and the nitrate anion (NH_4NO_3) that provides a concentrated source of N (34-0-0). For conifers, it is a perfect balance between the two principal forms of nitrogen used by plants. It is a preferred source of nitrogen for Christmas trees in regions where AN is readily available.

When AN is dissolved in the soil solution it produces a strongly acidic reaction. To neutralize this acid, an amount of lime equal to half the weight of AN is required. However, this extra acid is generally not a problem in plantations that have been limed. If changes in soil reaction are apt to be a problem, AN can be mixed with a coarse limestone at two parts AN to one part lime. Lime-coated AN can also be purchased, but the extra cost may be prohibitive.

Ammonium nitrate dissociates readily in water and can be used as a foliar spray. Although not a common method of application in plantations, foliar sprays can be used to correct deficiencies quickly or to treat nursery beds. Solution concen-

Table 9-2. Composition of principal fertilizer materials. Used with permission of the Fertilizer Handbook (63).

Material	Nitrogen %	Available Phosphate % P₂O₅	Potash % K₂O	Calcium %	Magnesium %	Sulfur %	Chlorine %	Copper %	Manganese %	Zinc %	Boron %	Approximate Calcium Carbonate equiv.₂ Lbs. per ton
NITROGEN												
Ammonia, Anhydrous.	82	—	—	—	—	—	—	—	—	—	—	−2,960
Ammonia, Aqua	16-25	—	—	—	—	—	—	—	—	—	—	−720 to −1,080
Ammonium nitrate	33.5	—	—	—	—	—	—	—	—	.01	—	−1,180
Ammonium nit.-limestone mixtures	20.5	—	—	7.3	4.4	.4	.4	—	—	—	—	0
Ammonium sulfate	21	—	—	.3	—	23.7	.5	.3	—	.1	—	−2,200
Ammonium sulfate-nitrate	26	—	—	—	—	15.1	—	—	—	—	—	−1,700
Calcium cyanamide	21	—	—	38.5	.06	.3	.2	—	.04	—	—	+1,260
Calcium nitrate	15	—	—	19.4	1.5	.02	.2	.02	—	—	—	++400
Nitrogen solutions	21-49	—	—	—	—	—	—	—	—	—	—	−750 to −1,760
Sodium nitrate	16	—	.2	.1	.05	.07	.4	.07	—	—	.01	+580
Urea	46	—	—	—	—	—	—	—	—	—	—	−1,680
Urea-form	38	—	—	—	—	—	—	—	—	—	—	−1,360
PHOSPHATE												
Basic slag, Open hearth	—	8-12[3]	—	29.0	3.4	.3	—	—	2.2	—	—	+1,000
Bone meal	2-4.5	22-28[4]	.2	20-25	.4	.1	.2	—	—	.02	—	+400 to 500
Phosphoric acid	—	52-60[5]	—	—	—	—	—	—	—	—	—	−1000 to −1400
Rock phosphate	—	—	—	33.2	.2	.3	.1	—	.03	.01	—	+200
Superphosphate, Normal	—	18-20	.2	20.4	.2	11.9	.3	.01	.01	—	—	0
Superphosphate, Concentrated	—	42-50	.4	13.6	.3	1.4	—	.01	.01	.01	.01	0
Superphosphoric acid	—	69-76	—	—	—	—	—	—	—	—	—	—

70

POTASH / MULTIPLE NUTRIENT materials — composition (%)

Material	N	P_2O_5	K_2O	Ca	Mg	S	Cl					Acid/base (lb $CaCO_3$)
POTASH												
Potassium chloride (muriate)	—	—	60-62	.1	.1	—	47.0	—	—	—	.03	0
Potassium magnesium sulfate	—	—	22	—	11.2	22.7	1.5	—	—	—	—	0
Potassium sulfate	—	—	50	.7	1.2	17.6	2.1	.001	—	—	.002	0
MULTIPLE NUTRIENT												
Ammoniated superphosphate	3-6	18-20	—	17.2	—	12	—	—	—	—	—	— 140
Ammonium phosphate-nitrate	27	15	—	—	—	—	—	—	—	—	—	—1240
Ammonium phosphate-sulfate	13-16	20-39	.2	.3	.1	15.4	.1	.02	.2	.02	.03	—1520 to 2260
Diammonium phosphate	16-21	48-53	—	—	—	—	—	.02	—	.03	.02	—1250 to —1,550
Monoammonium phosphate	11	48	.2	1.1	.3	2.2	.1	.02	.2	.03	.03	—1,300
Nitric phosphates	14-22	10-22	—	8-10	.1	2-3.6	1-12.0	—	—	—	.13	—300 to —500
Nitrate of soda-potash	15	—	14	—	—	—	.5	—	—	—	.10	+ 550
Potassium nitrate	13	—	44	.6	.2	—	1.1	.12	—	—	.16	+ 520
Wood ashes	—	1.8	5.5	23.3	2.2	.4	.2	.12	.76	.20	.10	+++
Blast furnace slag	—	1.7	.6	29.3	3.8	1.4	.3	.001	1.02	.001	.01	+++
Dolomite	—	—	—	21.5	11.4	.3	—	—	—	—	.01	+1,960
Gypsum	—	—	.5	22.5	.4	16.8	—	—	—	—	—	0
Kieserite (emjeo)	—	—	—	1.6	18.2	—	.3	—	.11	—	—	0
Limestone	—	—	.3	31.7	3.4	.1	—	.004	.48	.05	.003	+1,800
Lime-sulfur solution	—	—	—	6.7	—	23.8	—	—	—	—	—	0
Magnesium sulfate (Epsom salt)	—	—	—	2.2	10.5	14.0	.4	—	—	—	—	0
Sulfur	—	—	—	—	—	30-99.6	—	—	—	—	—	—1900 to —6,320

[1] Most of the percentages larger than one of N, P_2O_5, and K_2O are the usual guarantees. Where more than one grade is sold, the range is indicated by two members separated by a dash. The rest of the percentages are averages compiled by A. L. Mehring from many published analyses. [2] Ind. Eng. Chem. Anal. Ed. 5, 229-34 and other sources. A minus sign indicates the number of pounds of calcium carbonate needed to neutralize acid formed when 1 ton of the material is added to the soil. A plus sign indicates basic materials, and a zero physiologically neutral materials. [3] By the 2% citric acid method. [4] Total P_2O_5. All of the P_2O_5 in natural organics is considered available. [5] 30-36% total P_2O_5, which is relatively unavailable in some soils.

trations should be formulated at no higher than 10% (by weight) to prevent burning. Higher concentrations can be used when trees are dormant and when surfactants are mixed with the solution to improve wetability.

Growers who store AN must do so with care. It is hygroscopic, which means that it attracts moisture and is subject to caking. It is also a strong oxidant that can become explosive (see section 13.2). In fact, a mixture of AN and oil can be detonated and some farmers use it for blasting. Sacks of AN stored on an oil-soaked floor of an equipment shed can be dangerous, especially when smokers are around.

Two other common sources of ammonium are mono-ammonium phosphate (MAP: 11-48-0) and diammonium phosphate (DAP: 21-53-0). They are discussed in this section as phosphate sources, although both are excellent sources of N and P. Both forms are acid-forming, MAP more so than DAP, requiring 60–80% of their weight in lime to neutralize acidity, although the extra acidity is usually not a problem. Other ammoniated phosphate sources are available as well, but they may be expensive.

Ammonium sulfate (21-0-0) is a strongly acid source of N that is used most often on soils with a neutral or basic reaction (Table 9-2). It is a good source of S for soils lacking in this element. Plantations that are suffering from lime-induced nutrient deficiencies may benefit from the acid-forming characteristics of ammonium sulfate.

9.1.2 Urea Nitrogen

In terms of cost per unit, urea $\{CO(NH_2)_2\}$ is usually the cheapest source of N. It is produced by reacting ammonia with carbon dioxide, resulting in the most concentrated granular source of N (46-0-0) available. Its reaction in the soil is initially basic, but under warm soil conditions that favor the action of organisms which convert ammonium to nitrate, the ultimate reaction is acidic. Table 9-2 shows that an application of urea requires about 84% of its weight in lime to neutralize acidity. This figure is probably high for most instances since soils vary in the rate at which ammonium is converted to nitrate. Also, on a acid, cool soil, urea may have a slightly base-forming effect, raising pH slightly.

Urea applied during the growing season to bare soil or sod rapidly changes to NH_4 and ammonia gas. Gaseous losses of N can be substantial. When conditions are right, up to 20–30% of N applied as urea can be volatilized as ammonia. Surface applications to warm, wet soils and sod will promote losses. Urea mixed with formaldehyde, called urea-form, and sulfur coated urea will slow the conversion to ammonia and improve N efficiency, but both of these fertilizers are expensive. Growers who use pure urea must do so with care. In addition to the potential for gaseous losses, poor placement and high doses can kill seedlings and young trees or cause fertilizer burn. Coated urea is less apt to cause damage, but fertilizer granules should be kept off foliage as much as possible.

Urea dissociates readily in water so it is commonly applied in greenhouses and other intensively cultured crops as a foliar spray. Solutions of urea are discussed further in section 10.1.

9.1.3 Nitrate Nitrogen

In addition to ammonium nitrate, there are other sources of N supplied by the nitrate anion (NO_3). Calcium nitrate (15-0-0), sodium nitrate (16-0-0) and potassium nitrate (13-0-44) are three common N sources. All are base-forming substances that tend to raise soil pH rather than lower it, as is the case with ammonium sources. Of the three, potassium nitrate is most commonly used in Christmas trees, but principally as a source of K.

Although nitrate is immediately available to plants, it is not held in the soil and is subject to leaching. Nitrates should not be applied when heavy rains are expected. Nor should they be used in high doses near drinking wells or anywhere they are apt to leach rapidly into ground water supplies. As was mentioned earlier, nitrate sources of N should be supplemented with ammonium to achieve the best results.

9.2 Phosphorus Sources

Virtually all phosphate is obtained from deposits of the mineral apatite, found in geological formations that are actually uplifted ancient sea bottoms. Large deposits are located in Florida and other parts of the Southeast, and in the Western U.S.

Rock phosphate is treated with heat and acid to break strong chemical bonds that exist with fluorine, chlorine or carbon. Most phosphate fertilizer materials are reaction products of rock phosphate and sulfuric or phosphoric acid. Although sources of P are classified according to the amount of P_2O_5 that is available (either soluble in water or a weak acid), the principal forms of P found in soils and used by plants are quite different. Called primary ($H_2PO_4^-$) and secondary (HPO_4^{--}) orthophosphates, under most conditions these ions are rapidly precipitated with iron and aluminum in acid soils, and calcium in basic soils (see Section 7.1.3). As a result, soil P does not move very readily and if soil chemistry is not favorable, P can be locked up and unavailable to plants. Therefore, correct placement of phosphate is crucial.

Unlike nitrogen which has three different forms of N, fertilizer phosphorus is available in only one form—the phosphate anion (P_2O_5). This anion is combined with either calcium or ammonium to form superphosphates and ammonium phosphates.

9.2.1 Superphosphates

There are two types of superphosphate, ordinary or normal (0-20- 0) and triple or concentrated superphosphate (0-46-0). Of the two, triple is more commonly used and usually a better buy in terms of cost per unit of P. Both are ultimately neutral in reaction with soil. However, the initial reaction of superphosphate with soil water results in a very low pH in the immediate vicinity of fertilizer particles. Superphosphate in contact with tree roots will cause damage and seedling death if concentrations are high enough.

As noted above, when soil conditions are acid or basic, phosphate will be locked up, usually within millimeters of the fertilizer granules. The degree to which this occurs is a function of soil pH. The ideal pH for optimum P availability is about 5.5–6.5. Even when conditions are favorable, P does not move appreciably in the soil, particularly where aluminum, iron and calcium levels are high . Unlike N, surface applications of phosphate rarely penetrate more than an inch in all but the most sandy, inert mineral soils. As a result, soil erosion in areas that have had surface applications of phosphate can cause tremendous losses of P. When phosphate gets into rivers and lakes, water quality usually suffers.

9.2.2 Ammonium Phosphates

There are two common ammonium phosphates, mono- (11-48-0) and diammonium phosphate (16-48-0). The grades of each may vary slightly in their proportions of N and P. The primary difference between the superphosphates and ammonium phosphates is that the later are acid-forming. An amount of lime equal to 60–75% of the weight of ammonium phosphates must be applied to neutralize the acid formed by these compounds. However, they are both excellent sources of N and P. In some parts of the country, ammoniated phosphates may be easier to obtain than superphosphates because they are cheaper per unit of nutrient to ship and are easily blended into mixed fertilizers.

9.3 Potassium Sources

Potassium is obtained from salt beds formed when ancient seas evaporated. The most extensive deposits are located at various depths below the surface in Canada and the USSR. A mineral called sylvite, which is mostly potassium chloride, is the principal raw material used to manufacture fertilizer K. Once K-bearing ore is obtained, it does not require large expenditures of energy to refine it, as is the case with rock phosphate. Potassium is refined by dissolving ore in water and allowing potassium chloride to precipitate.

The most common K fertilizer is potassium chloride, known as muriate of potash (0-0-60). A very high chlorine content makes this material unsuitable for use in the Christmas tree plantation, especially when trees are first established. Salts of potassium with sulfate, magnesium & sulfate, or nitrate are better sources of K.

Potassium magnesium sulfate (0-0-22) and potassium sulfate (0-0- 50) are neutral in reaction with soil, while potassium nitrate (13-0-44) is slightly base-forming. Of the three, potassium magnesium sulfate is the most commonly used in the Christmas tree plantation. It is an excellent source of K while providing about 11% magnesium and 23% sulfate. Quite often when K is limiting in the soil, Mg is limiting as well. When this is the case, potassium magnesium sulfate is a good choice.

Potassium nitrate is a good source of nitrate anions to supplement a urea application, or N supplied by one of the ammonium phosphates.

9.4 Calcium, Magnesium and Sulfur Sources

The most common source of Ca and Mg is agricultural limestone. Although proportions vary depending upon the source of limestone, usually about 32% by weight is Ca (not CaO) and 3–5% is Mg. Dolomitic limestone, common in some

TABLE 9-3 Suggested Applications of Ordinary Powdered Sulfur to Reduce the pH of 100 Square Feet of an 8 inch Layer of Sand or Loam Soil

| Original pH | Pints of Powdered Sulfur, for Desired pH | | | | | | | | | |
| | 4.5 | | 5.0 | | 5.5 | | 6.0 | | 6.5 | |
	Sand	Loam	Sand	Loam	Sand	Loam	Sand	Loam	Sand	Loam
5.0	2/3	2								
5.5	1-1/3	4	2/3	2						
6.0	2	3-1/2	1-1/3	4	2/3	2				
6.5	2-1/2	8	2	5-1/2	1-1/3	4	2/3	2		
7.0	3	10	2-1/2	8	2	5-1/2	1-1/3	4	2/3	2

TABLE 9-3. taken from the 1957 Yearbook of Agriculture, p. 678, "Home gardens and Lawns" by C. E. Kellogg, used with permission of J. Wiley.

localities, has about 22% Ca and 11% Mg. It is important to note that these elements are rarely lacking in Christmas tree plantations that have been limed. A more thorough discussion of liming materials is in section 9.6.

Most often applications of limestone are prescribed to

affect an increase in pH and to reduce the amount of soil acidity. Its effect on Ca and Mg supplies is almost never an important consideration. Ca, Mg and S supplies can, however, be increased without affecting pH. Gypsum is about 22% Ca by weight and 17% sulfur. Its reaction with the soil is neutral. Potassium magnesium sulfate also has a neutral reaction and about 11% Mg and 23% sulfur. In most parts of the country, particularly in the Northeast, deposition of S from industrial emissions provides more than enough of this element.

Sulfur is commonly used to lower soil pH. It is an acidifying agent, opposite the effect of limestone. Table 9-3 shows sulfur amounts that must be applied to soils of different texture to lower pH.

9.5 Micronutrient Sources

Micronutrient supplies are usually adequate for Christmas tree culture on most sites. That is not to say micronutrient deficiencies do not occur from time to time. The most common cause of micronutrient deficiency in Christmas tree plantations results from excessive liming. When single applications of limestone exceed two tons per acre, the potential for lime- induced deficiencies are high. Most micronutrients are positively charged cations that precipitate as insoluble compounds when soil pH is raised. The optimum soil-in-water pH for micronutrient availability is 5.0–5.5. Once the effect of limestone has moved through the soil, after six months to a year or more depending upon soil texture, the pH of upper soil horizons begin to decrease and micronutrient availability increases.

Applications of micronutrients are rarely called for, and when necessary they must be applied with care. Since plants use these elements in such small quantities, the range between deficiency and toxicity is often narrow. Also, unless the underlying problem is corrected first, soil applications of micronutrients will be locked up in the same way that natural supplies are held.

Although micronutrient deficiencies are difficult to establish in Christmas trees, known deficiencies are usually corrected with a foliar spray. There are many different sprays available, some of which are listed in Appendix D, along with the name and address of the manufacturer. The nutrients are usually chelated, which means that the metals are combined with an organic structure that protects solubility. When micronutrients are applied to the soil, they must be chelated to protect them from getting bound into insoluble compounds.

9.6 Liming Materials

Limestone is a soil amendment usually prescribed to improve soil chemistry allowing the site to achieve its full potential to make nutrient elements available to plants. Related discussions on soil pH and the effects of liming are found in sections 4.3, 8.1 and 10.4. The purpose of this section is to describe the types of available liming materials and the rate and degree to which they can effect an increase in soil pH.

Liming materials are categorized on the basis of their neutralizing value. Called the "calcium carbonate equivalent" (CCE), it is the capacity of a unit weight of a liming material to neutralize soil acidity. Calcium carbonate is a standard material against which others are compared because it is the most prevalent compound in limestone deposits found throughout the U.S. The CCE of pure calcium carbonate is 100. The most common liming material, called agricultural limestone, is usually composed of carbonates of Ca and Mg in varying proportions. Agricultural limestone may provide 3–5% Mg. When Mg content is high, the material is called dolomitic limestone or dolomite. Dolomite has a CCE of 109.

Sometimes the acid-neutralizing capability of a liming material is expressed in terms of calcium oxide equivalents, since calcium oxide is the strongest commercial liming material available.

Technically, the term "lime" applies only to calcium oxide which has a CCE of 179. In other words, an equal amount of calcium oxide, also known as burned lime or quicklime, will neutralize 79% more acid than calcium carbonate. Quicklime and hydrated lime or builder's lime (CCE = 136), are very strong base-forming materials that are much more expensive than calcium carbonate. Quicklime is marketed as "liquid lime", a suspension of lime in water that is easily transported and sprayed on fields. Liquid lime is very fast acting, but it can raise soil pH levels dangerously high and the effect does not last as long as powdered agricultural limestone. Ground limestone takes longer to effect a change in pH but it is longer lasting and safer to use. It is impossible to raise soil pH above 8.0 even with massive doses of agricultural limestone, whereas liquid lime can raise pH considerably higher than this for short periods of time.

Limestone is very slow-acting. A surface application of limestone may take up to 10 years or more to effect a change in pH at a depth of six inches. Time since application and particle size, not total amount of limestone applied, determine the volume of soil that can react with limestone. Since the neutralizing effect of limestone travels through the soil like a wave, usually by the time the lower soil horizons are influenced, the upper horizons have become more acidic.

Wood ash is also a good liming material that supplies small amounts of K in addition to Ca and Mg. It is very basic, having a high CCE, and is fast acting. Wood ash must be used in the plantation with care. Too much will raise soil pH in the rooting zone far above optimum and trees will suffer.

The timing and placement of limestone applications is the subject of section 10.4.

9.7 Mixed Fertilizers

Most fertilizers are marketed to the public as mixed blends available in various grades. Substances that provide N,P and K are known as "complete" fertilizers, one of the most common of which is 10-10-10. When the proportions are equal, the fertilizer is said to be "balanced."

Occasionally the unit price of these bagged blends is fairly reasonable. However, usually the cost per unit of nutrient is considerably higher than the cost of nutrients in equal weights of fertilizer materials purchased separately. Growers who purchase fertilizers should do so, not through garden supply stores, but through a fertilizer dealer who has the capability to blend fertilizer materials into any ratio the customer requires. Mixing of fertilizers is complicated and should be left

TABLE 9-4 Conversion Factors for Reagent Grade Materials (fertilizer grades will differ). Used with permission of Fertilizer Handbook (63).

To find the equivalent of one material, A, in terms of another, B, multiply the amount of A by the factor in column "A to B." To find the equivalent of material B in terms of A, multiply the amount of B by the factor in column "B to A."

A	B	Multiply A to B	B to A
Ammonia (NH_3)	Nitrogen (N)	0.8224	1.2159
Nitrate (NO_3)	Nitrogen (N)	0.2259	4.4266
Protein (crude)	Nitrogen (N)	0.1600	6.2500
Ammonium nitrate (NH_4NO_3)	Nitrogen (N)	0.3500	2.8572
Ammonium sulfate [$(NH_4)_2SO_4$]	Nitrogen (N)	0.2120	4.7168
Calcium nitrate [$Ca(NO_3)_2$]	Nitrogen (N)	0.1707	5.8572
Potassium nitrate (KNO_3)	Nitrogen (N)	0.1386	7.2176
Sodium nitrate ($NaNO_3$)	Nitrogen (N)	0.1648	6.0679
Monoammonium phosphate ($NH_4H_2PO_4$)	Nitrogen (N)	0.1218	8.2118
Diammonium phosphate [$(NH_4)_2HPO_4$]	Nitrogen (N)	0.2121	4.7138
Urea [$(NH_2)_2CO$]	Nitrogen (N)	0.4665	2.1437
Phosphoric acid (P_2O_5)[1]	Phosphorus (P)	0.4364	2.2914
Phosphate (PO_4)	Phosphorus (P)	0.3261	3.0662
Monoammonium phosphate ($NH_4H_2PO_4$)	Phosphoric acid (P_2O_5)[1]	0.6170	1.6207
Diammonium phosphate [$(NH_4)_2HPO_4$]	Phosphoric acid (P_2O_5)[1]	0.5374	1.8607
Monocalcium phosphate [$Ca(H_2PO_4)_2$]	Phosphoric acid (P_2O_5)[1]	0.6068	1.6479
Dicalcium phosphate ($CaHPO_4 \cdot 2H_2O$)	Phosphoric acid (P_2O_5)[1]	0.4124	2.4247
Tricalcium phosphate [$Ca_3(PO_4)_2$]	Phosphoric acid (P_2O_5)[1]	0.4581	2.1829
Potash (K_2O)	Potassium (K)	0.8301	1.2046
Muriate of potash (KCl)	Potash (K_2O)	0.6317	1.5828
Sulfate of potash (K_2SO_4)	Potash (K_2O)	0.5405	1.8499
Potassium nitrate (KNO_3)	Potash (K_2O)	0.4658	2.1466
Potassium carbonate (K_2CO_3)	Potash (K_2O)	0.6816	1.4672
Gypsum ($CaSO_4 \cdot 2H_2O$)	Calcium sulfate ($CaSO_4$)	0.7907	1.2647
Gypsum ($CaSO_4 \cdot 2H_2O$)	Calcium (Ca)	0.2326	4.3000
Gypsum ($CaSO_4 \cdot 2H_2O$)	Calcium oxide (CaO)	0.3257	3.0702
Calcium oxide (CaO)	Calcium (Ca)	0.7147	1.3992
Calcium carbonate ($CaCO_3$)	Calcium (Ca)	0.4004	2.4973
Calcium carbonate ($CaCO_3$)	Calcium oxide (CaO)	0.5604	1.7848
Calcium carbonate ($CaCO_3$)	Calcium hydroxide [$Ca(OH)_2$]	0.7403	1.3508
Calcium hydroxide [$Ca(OH)_2$]	Calcium (Ca)	0.5409	1.8487

(Continued)

A	B	Multiply A to B	B to A
Magnesium oxide (MgO)	Magnesium (Mg)	0.6032	1.6579
Magnesium sulfate (MgSO$_4$)	Magnesium (Mg)	0.2020	4.9501
Epsom salts (MgSO$_4$•7H$_2$O)	Magnesium (Mg)	0.0987	10.1356
Sulfate (SO$_4$)	Sulfur (S)	0.3333	3.0000
Ammonium sulfate [(NH$_4$)$_2$SO$_4$]	Sulfur (S)	0.2426	4.1211
Gypsum (CaSO$_4$•2H$_2$O)	Sulfur (S)	0.1860	5.3750
Magnesium sulfate (MgSO$_4$)	Sulfur (S)	0.3190	3.1350
Potassium sulfate (K$_2$SO$_4$)	Sulfur (S)	0.1837	5.4438
Sulfuric acid (H$_2$SO$_4$)	Sulfur (S)	0.3269	3.0587
Borax (Na$_2$B$_4$O$_7$•10H$_2$O)	Boron (B)	0.1134	8.8129
Boron trioxide (B$_2$O$_3$)	Boron (B)	0.3107	3.2181
Sodium tetraborate pentahydrate (Na$_2$B$_4$O$_7$•5H$_2$O)	Boron (B)	0.1485	6.7315
Sodium tetraborate anhydrous (Na$_2$B$_4$O$_7$)	Boron (B)	0.2150	4.6502
Cobalt nitrate [Co(NO$_3$)$_2$•6H$_2$O]	Cobalt (Co)	0.2025	4.9383
Cobalt sulfate (CoSO$_4$•7H$_2$O)	Cobalt (Co)	0.2097	4.7690
Cobalt sulfate (CoSO$_4$)	Cobalt (Co)	0.3802	2.6299
Copper sulfate (CuSO$_4$)	Copper (Cu)	0.3981	2.5119
Copper sulfate (CuSO$_4$•5H$_2$O)	Copper (Cu)	0.2545	3.9293
Ferric sulfate [Fe$_2$(SO$_4$)$_3$]	Iron (Fe)	0.2793	3.5804
Ferrous sulfate (FeSO$_4$)	Iron (Fe)	0.3676	2.7203
Ferrous sulfate (FeSO$_4$•7H$_2$O)	Iron (Fe)	0.2009	4.9776
Manganese sulfate (MnSO$_4$)	Manganese (Mn)	0.3638	2.7486
Manganese sulfate (MnSO$_4$•4H$_2$O)	Manganese (Mn)	0.2463	4.0602
Sodium molybdate (Na$_2$MoO$_4$•2H$_2$O)	Molybdenum (Mo)	0.3965	2.5218
Sodium nitrate (NaNO$_3$)	Sodium (Na)	0.2705	3.6970
Sodium chloride (NaCl)	Sodium (Na)	0.3934	2.5417
Zinc oxide (ZnO)	Zinc (Zn)	0.8034	1.2447
Zinc sulfate (ZnSO$_4$)	Zinc (Zn)	0.4050	2.4693
Zinc sulfate (ZnSO$_4$•H$_2$O)	Zinc (Zn)	0.3643	2.7449

[1]Also called phosphoric acid anhydride, phosphorus pentoxide, available phosphoric acid.

TABLE 9-4, continued

to the dealer. However, the grower must specify the materials, or nutrient sources, to be used.

For mixing small amounts at the plantation, growers need to remember that the fertilizer grade is the percentage by weight of N, P_2O_5 or K_2O that a substance provides. For example, 100 pounds of triple super phosphate, 0-46-0, provides 46 pounds of P_2O_5.

Table 9-4 lists the conversion factors to find the oxide or elemental equivalents of some common fertilizer materials.

To blend 200 lbs. of 12-10-8 using triple superphosphate (0-46-0), potassium magnesium sulfate (0-0-22 plus 11% Mg and 23% S), and ammonium nitrate (34-0-0), combine the following amounts:

Solve for Required Raw Material Amount...

$$\frac{\text{Raw Material Grade} \quad X \quad \text{Req. Raw Material Amount}}{\text{Total Weight of Blend}} = \text{Grade of nutrient in blend}$$

For nitrogen:

$$\frac{0.34 \quad X \quad (\text{Amount})}{200 \text{ lbs.}} = .12$$

0.34 (Amount) = 24

Amount = 71 lbs. of 34-0-0

For phosphate:

0.46 (Amount) = 20

Amount = 43 lbs. of 0-46-0

For potassium oxide:

0.22 (Amount) = 16

Amount = 73 lbs. of 0-0-22

Total of raw materials = 189 lbs.

Bulk filler (limestone)= 11 lbs.

Total Blend Weight = 200 lbs.

(This blend also provides 4% magnesium and 8% sulfur by weight. It also provides a small amount of calcium (2%) by virtue of the filler)

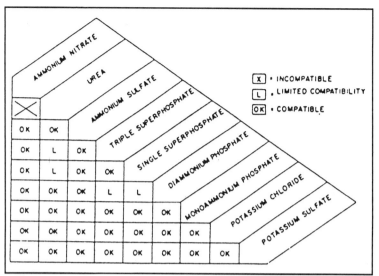

Figure 9-2. Chemical compatibility of blend materials. Used with permission of the Farm Chemicals Handbook (18).

When materials supplying more than one source of a nutrient are used to figure blends, the calculations become a little more complicated and are best left to the dealer. The grower must, however, insist that the dealer use the requested materials. Otherwise, the mix will be formulated out of the materials that are easiest for the dealer.

Some substances should not be blended. For example, when urea is mixed with ammonium nitrate, the blend is extremely hygroscopic, ie., it attracts moisture from the atmosphere. The blend will cake and make handling very difficult. Figure 9-2 shows the relative compatibility of fertilizer materials that are commonly blended.

9.8 Manures

Animal manures can provide essential nutrients, but the concentration of elements is very low (Table 9-5). Thus, manures are usually costly. For example, N supplied by cattle manure may cost as much as five times more than N supplied by ammonium nitrate (2). Also, handling is difficult, and cattle, horse and sheep manure contain seeds of grasses and

MANURE COMPOSITION					
Constituent	Cattle %	Horse %	Sheep %	Swine %	Chicken %
N	0.53	0.55	0.89	0.63	0.89
P_2O_5	.29	.27	.48	.46	.48
K_2O	.48	.57	.83	.41	.83
Ca	.29	.27	.21	.19	.38
Mg	.11	.11	.13	.03	.13
Cu	.00079	.00079	.00079	.00016	.0006
Mn	.003	.003	.003	.0008	.003
Zn	.0016	.002	.002	.0006	.0021
Cl	.03	.08	.08	.03	.08
S	.036	.036	.06	.03	.06
B	.016	.016	.016	.0005	.016
Org. matter	16.74	27.06	30.70	15.50	30.70
Moisture	81.33	68.85	64.82	77.56	64.82
Ash	2.06	6.70	4.72	6.02	4.72

TABLE 9-5. Manure Composition. Used with permission of the Farm Chemicals Handbook (18).

forbs that may be noxious. A manure mulch will improve water relations around the plant and also have a positive effect on the nutrient holding capacity of the soil.

If manures must be purchased, they are usually impractical. However, if a free source of good quality, seasoned manure is readily available, it may provide most of the nutrition required by the plantation, provided the cost of labor and handling is not too significant. Growers should consider the fact that most free sources of manure have been mishandled so their fertilizer value is minimal. Some manures, such as from race tracks, have been limed to reduce the smell and may be much too basic for Christmas trees.

9.9 Slow-release Fertilizers

Fertilizers that have been treated to decrease solubility and activity in the soil are called "slow-release." These materials take the form of tablets, packets and plastic-coated granules that can be dropped into the planting hole. Since trees use nutrients at a slower rate than most crop plants, the logic behind slow-release fertilizers is obvious. However, these substances are costly. Compared to the cost per unit of nutrient from other sources, slow-release fertilizers are five to ten times more expensive.

A recent study on the effects of slow-release fertilizers on Christmas trees in Indiana discovered that tablets and packets, used according to the manufacturer's directions and costing $90–$350 per acre, had very little effect on height growth or color even after four years. The least expensive treatment—an application of 0.5 ounce per seeding of 20-10-10—cost only $20–$30 per acre and provided the best results (43). A similar study with Douglas fir confirmed that fertilizer release rate at the time of planting has little effect on growth and no advantages over immediately available nutrient sources (61).

10.0 PLACEMENT AND TIMING OF FERTILIZER APPLICATIONS

Fertilizers must be applied to the proper place and at the correct time to achieve optimum effectiveness and efficiency. Poor placement and timing can cause excessive nutrient losses—with the possibility of polluting water supplies—and can also result in tree damage.

The purpose of this section is to discuss timing and placement considerations for different fertilizer sources commonly used with Christmas trees. Fertilizer amounts are discussed in section 12.0.

10.1 Nitrogen

Nitrogen sources are usually applied to the soil or sod surface as a broadcast over the entire site, or solely around the base of each tree. Some growers fertilizer just the tree rows, and some will apply a measured dose mostly on one side of the tree near the drip-line of the crown (Figure 10-1). The nutrient ions dissociate quickly when it rains and move readily into the soil and the rooting zone. However, to avoid the potential for chemical damage to trees, N-containing fertilizers should not be broadcast or applied in concentrated bands any closer to young tree stems than 6 inches. Applications concentrated on one side of the tree should not be located directly above the main body of the root system. Also, when N is applied mostly on the down-hill side of trees, its effect will be less than when applied on the up-hill side. The idea is to apply N so that the initially strong chemical reaction with the soil does not damage roots. Yet the application must be close enough to allow roots to grow readily into the enriched volume of soil. On older trees, N-fertilizers are used to best effect when broadcast around the drip-line of the crown and not directly under the branches.

However, small amounts of N broadcast evenly inside the drip-line of the tree will usually not cause any burning. It is when applications are concentrated in one area over the root system that burning can occur.

Only about 10–20% of a single broadcast application of N

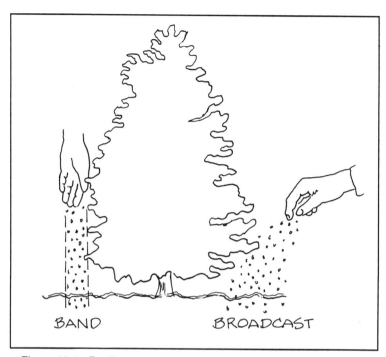

Figure 10-1. Fertilizer application by hand.

is taken up and used by trees (13, 44). The balance is tied up in soil organisms, in other plants, and a portion—sometimes a large portion on sandy soils—is leached out of the rooting zone by rainfall. Leaching is particularly rapid with nitrate N. Using organic sources of N, or small but frequent applications of inorganic sources, will lessen losses from leaching.

Grasses and forbs in the plantation usually thrive on N applications. Some studies suggest that fertilizer applications are wasted without weed control. Flourishing weeds compete with Christmas trees for light and space. They can overtop and suppress seedlings, or cause premature mortality of lower branches on older trees. Although the physical effects of increased weed growth are real and potentially damaging or fatal, it is probably more correct to say that the positive effects of fertilizer applications on trees are delayed rather than lost. Eventually the nutrients held by grasses and forbs are cycled back into the soil where they will become available to trees. Notwithstanding, when fertilizers stimulate weeds that can reduce tree growth or damage foliage, some form of weed control is necessary. Mowing and mulching are acceptable alternatives to herbicides.

Where the effect of weed stimulation is apt to damage trees, nitrogen fertilizers can be applied in a band near the drip-line of tree crowns. To avoid concentrating tree roots all in one area, the band should be shifted each time. Urea and ammonium nitrate can even be used to kill especially noxious weeds when applied in a concentrated pattern over the plant's root system. This method is very effective when vegetation is wet. However, N losses from volatilization of urea may be excessive. When fertilizer granules are apt to lodge in tree foliage, conditions should be dry and foliage dormant to avoid needle damage. Granules should be brushed from foliage as much as possible.

Nitrogen sources, with the exception of slow-release, should never be put into the bottom of planting holes. The potential for root damage from salts and the volatilization of ammonia gas is too great. In fact, surface applications of N around seedlings should be very light—a half ounce or less of ammonium nitrate per seedling—and placed at least six inches away from the stem in the year of planting. Many growers do not use N at all in the first year since the seedlings usually come from the nurseries with a good supply. Also, when planting seedlings in herbicide-killed sod, organic N released from the sod is usually sufficient for the first year. However, if N content of seedling foliage at the time of planting is less than 1.5% (dry weight), an N application may be called for. The nursery should be able to supply a foliar analysis of its seedlings. Although do not be surprised if they hesitate; chances are they have never been asked by a Christmas tree grower to provide a copy of the analysis.

Adequate N supplies are important early in the growing season. Just before buds begin to expand, the tree lays down new structures of microscopic proportions. These new structures determine not how the tree will grow in the current season, but how it will grow in the next season. Adequate nutrition stimulates more development which translates into increased growth in the following year. Although this is a good time for optimum nutrition, it is risky to have readily soluble N sources on the site. Wet soils and spring rains can cause tremendous N losses in early spring. Organic sources of N are not as susceptible to leaching as inorganic sources.

Nitrogen applications should be delayed until after early spring rains. An alternative in the northern states is a late fall application of urea. Cold temperatures prevent the conversion of urea to ammonium, so potential over-winter losses are minor. When conditions warm in the spring, ammonium is gradually released and available to trees. The fall application of urea should not be a heavy dose, rather it should be about one-third of the total to be applied over the course of the next growing season. Too much N early in the spring causes excessive stimulation that can make trees spindly and difficult to shape. However, some growers use high doses of N (up to 4 ounces per tree) in the early summer of the year trees are to be harvested to obtain a dark green hue.

Urea and ammonium nitrate can also be applied to foliage as a spray solution. Though not a common practice in the Christmas trees, N-sprays can quickly improve internal nitrogen concentrations. In one study, a 32% (by weight) spray solution at a rate of 50 lbs. of N per acre (as urea) raised internal concentrations of dormant Douglas fir foliage from 1.43% to 1.74% within 48 hours (41). This is a very high rate of application that may cause "burning". Solutions of 10% (by weight) urea are safe under most circumstances. If trees need to be greened-up in a hurry, foliar applications of urea during the growing season will work well.

On sandy soils, applications of granular-N should be light but more frequent. This means two or three applications rather than one large dose in late spring. Multiple applications of smaller doses improves N recovery on all types of soils. In northern climates, N applications should be suspended before the first of August. Late season N applications can promote succulent foliage that is easily damaged by early fall frosts. Some species, especially in the South, may flush at a time when buds should be resting. When the season is especially dry, nitrogen should be applied only sparingly. High N levels during drought years can be detrimental to growth and survival of young trees (60).

10.2 Phosphorus

Whenever possible, phosphates should either be mixed with the soil months before planting, or applied as a band in, not on top of, the soil at the time of planting. A "banded" application is when fertilizer is applied in narrow swaths to the soil. The objective of banding is to avoid soil mixing.

When conditions are acid and highly buffered (a pH below 5.0 in a fine textured soil with high levels of aluminum or iron), the preferred method of application is banding.

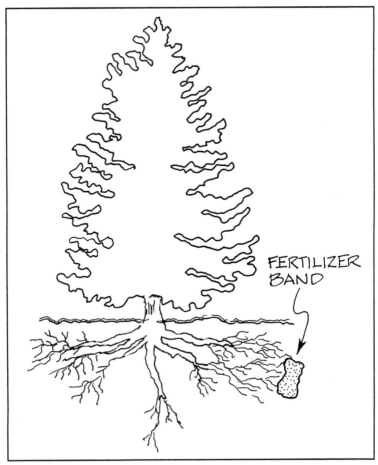

Figure 10-2. A soil band application of fertilizer.

Phosphates mixed with an acid soil will be quickly locked up and unavailable to trees. A band of phosphate, separated from the root system by at least 2 inches of soil, will create a concentrated pocket of P (Figure 10-2). Tree roots will grow into the vicinity of this pocket and extract a much larger portion of P than if this same amount were mixed with the soil.

Only rock phosphate or the superphosphates should be used in the planting hole. Ammoniated phosphates, especially diammonium phosphate, should not be used in the vicinity of tree roots. The possibilities of root damage from ammonia gas are too great.

Surface applications of phosphates will not be nearly as effective as below surface applications in many soils. When P is applied to the surface it promotes shallow rooting as tree roots grow toward phosphate sources in the top layers of soil. Although this is not necessarily bad, shallow roots are more susceptible to damage from misapplied fertilizers, chemicals and physical injuries.

An adequate source of P is very important early in the life of the plantation as it stimulates root development. On good soils one application at the time of establishment may be all that is required. There is also some evidence to suggest that phosphate will enhance the effects of other nutrients on plant growth. For example, an application of P may not yield a response. However, an application of P and N yields a better response than N alone. These types of interactions are the subject of section 11.0.

10.3 Potassium

On most soils, K sources act like ammonium. In fact, the potassium ion and ammonium ion, in addition to having the same positive charge, are about the same size.

Potassium sources can be applied to the soil surface. They dissociate quickly in water and move readily into the rooting zone. Most also have a high salt-index which means they can easily cause fertilizer burn. This is especially true of potassium nitrate. For this reason, K fertilizers are usually broadcast as a topdress around the drip-line of the tree. One application may be sufficient for the rotation, but favorable interactions with other elements may suggest more frequent applications. K sources should never be applied to the planting hole. The risk of salt damage to roots is too great. Also, potassium sources should be used sparingly during dry years.

Adequate supplies of K are important throughout the growing season. It can be applied at any time of the year, except when there is the possibility of it being washed off sloping sites before it has had a chance to move into the soil. Potassium magnesium sulfate (0-0-22) is an excellent source of K for Christmas trees.

10.4 Limestone

When limestone is applied to sod or the soil surface and not mixed in, it takes two to four years to alter soil pH in the upper few inches of soil, and 8–10 years to increase the pH to a depth of 6 inches. This is true regardless of the amount of lime applied. The acid-neutralizing effect of limestone moves like a wave through the soil, very slowly in fine textured soils. By the time a single application has increased pH at 6 inches, the top few inches are acid once again.

After plantation soils have been limed, future soil samples should be taken from the upper 4 inches. Including soil from lower depths may result in a pH reading that is lower than conditions in the rooting zone.

Limestone should be applied as much in advance of planting as is practical. When limestone is mixed with the soil it can effect a change in the pH of a volume of soil in as little as 6 months to 2 years. However, soil mixing is usually not practical for most growers. Nevertheless, some mixing does occur during planting if limestone has been applied beforehand.

Contrary to popular belief, agricultural limestone will not cause burning or damage to foliage so it can be applied at any time during the growing season. Foliage contact is not a problem. Late summer and fall applications are easier to schedule with commercial dealers because most of their business is in the spring. Limestone applications on frozen ground are acceptable. However, when applied on top of snow cover in hilly terrain, there is the possibility that a portion of the limestone will be lost due to runoff.

Single applications of limestone should not exceed a rate of two tons per acre. Higher rates will not speed up the reaction, but may cause lime-induced deficiencies of micronutrients. When the soil test calls for more than two tons per acre, the total should be split into two or three applications that are 6 months to a year apart. After the plantation is established and commercial applications are impractical (unless the layout of the plantation was designed to accommodate lime trucks) limestone can be broadcast between tree rows or over small trees. Application rates of limestone must be proportionally reduced or converted to pounds per square foot and the application to rows and trees adjusted accordingly. For example, if tree rows occupy 50% of the space on an acre, the limestone rate must be cut in half.

About 1/2 cup of limestone spread over each tree in a circular pattern that is 3 ft. in diameter supplies approximately 1,500 lbs. per acre. Single applications should not exceed this amount by too much regardless of the total amount of lime that needs to be applied. The best strategy for managing soil pH in the plantation is patience.

10.5 Secondary and Micronutrients

The secondary nutrients Ca, Mg and S are rarely in short supply in most Christmas tree plantations. These elements are also present in a variety of primary nutrient sources and atmospheric inputs of sulfur are high in many parts of the country. There are no special guidelines on timing and application of these elements, except as may be required to correct a known deficiency.

The special nature of micronutrient applications is discussed in section 9.5. If an application of micronutrients is necessary to overcome the effects of excessive liming, foliar application during the growing season is advisable. Micronutrient chelates can also be blended with other fertilizers and applied on a regular basis. However, as was pointed out earlier, micronutrients are generally not necessary, but some growers mix them in with other fertilizer materials just as a precautionary measure. Careful attention to application rates is necessary to avoid toxicities.

11.0 NUTRIENT INTERACTIONS

Understanding and predicting the positive and negative effects of interactions between nutrient elements in the soil is one of the most difficult aspects of plant nutrition. Negative interactions can cause nutrient deficiencies even when supplies of an element are adequate. Positive interactions result when an increase in the supply of one element increases the availability of another. Sometimes a negative interaction, also called "antagonism", under one set of circumstances is a positive interaction when conditions change. For example, when soil pH is increased with limestone, an increase in Ca supplies improves the availability of K. However, when Ca levels are too high, it competes with K for exchange sites on plant roots (37). High pH also causes an imbalance of Ca and K to P that can limit P utilization (12). This is especially true for acid-tolerant plants like conifers.

Many of the known nutrient interactions involve N. Since the effects of N on plant growth are studied more than any other element, it is not surprising that interactions involving N are discovered and reported more frequently than for other elements.

The principal inorganic forms of soil N are nitrate (NO_3) and ammonium (NH_4). The presence of NH_4 is known to enhance uptake of P (63). Urea, which breaks down into NH_4, will release larger quantities of soil P than ammonium nitrate, but the latter has a more positive effect on Ca and Mg availability (44). However, urea is believed to suppress the development of mycorrhizae more than ammonium nitrate. Acid soil conditions favor mycorrhizae and when soil pH is below 5.0, NO_3 may be used more efficiently than NH_4, but the nitrate ion is more common when soils are basic (20).

Conifers seem to grow best when both forms of N are present in the soil (15, 26). It is a delicate balance, though, because high levels of NH_4 will depress uptake of K, but when NO_3 levels are high, P levels can be depressed (36). Also, high amounts of NO_3 relative to NH_4 will increase the concentration of cations and organic anions in solution, blocking nutrient uptake and causing chlorosis in acid-tolerant conifers such as Scots pine (12). In some circumstances where K is limiting, N fertilization may result in a K deficiency (42). However, when soil K levels are high, a N deficiency can result even when soil supplies of it are adequate (38).

When N is applied to a soil that is lacking in Ca, no response or even growth reductions are possible suggesting a Ca–N antagonism (12). Notwithstanding, the acidifying or Ca- suppressing effects of ammonium-N sources have a positive effect on most micronutrients. But when soil pH is lowered, aluminum and iron tend to bind with P making it unavailable.

Ca and Mg are antagonists. An excessively high level of one element will limit the availability of the other. Excessively high Ca levels will also tie up P.

Mg and K appear to be antagonistic in foliage. High K levels will reduce Mg, and vice versa. Also, foliar K levels may be reduced when P levels are low, but the reverse situation does not appear to exist (59).

High levels of foliar N are known to reduce foliar P and K (59). However, fertilizer treatments that supply P and K in the absence of N may have no effect on foliage color and growth rate (57). When N is limiting there is a tendency for luxury consumption (see section 4.1.1) of P and K (27, 54).

N utilization in conifers has also been tied to S availability. When foliar S is low, trees may not respond to N applications (56). In this study, a constant ratio of foliar S to N of 0.03 is optimum for pine and Douglas fir. Note that this value is about one-third of the optimum ratio reported in Table 8-4. When foliar concentrations of S dropped below 400 ppm, response from N applications in this study were limited. Fortunately, in most parts of the country atmospheric inputs of S provide more than adequate supplies of this element. Sulfur deficiencies are more common in the Northwest U.S.

High and low N levels can cause stress in spruce and pine (4). Frost hardiness decreased when foliar N levels exceeded 1.8%, or when they were less than 1.5%. High levels of N with K and micronutrients, but without P, also caused premature shedding of needles and reduced stem growth.

N and P share a complex relationship. Applications of one without adequate supplies of the other may result in no response, or only a fraction of the potential response if supplies of both had been adequate. In many fertilizer studies with conifers, the main response was from N, or N with P. However, if foliar P levels get too high, trees may not respond to N applications (52). In one experiment, foliar N levels were reduced by P fertilization, and response to P was tied to adequate N supplies in Douglas fir (22).

In another experiment, the effect of N applications on balsam fir were improved when P was applied at the same time. Although increased growth rates were not attributable to P, the P- containing treatments resulted in better bud development (53). With Douglas fir seedlings an application of phosphate did not increase growth rate but it did improve survival (61).

The complex nature of nutrient interactions is one of the principal reasons why most of the nutrient related problems in Christmas tree plantations can be traced to careless use of fertilizers. Nutrient applications must take into account the current nutrient status of the soil and trees. They must also be properly balanced. A constant, balanced, low level of fertility is preferred to wild swings between high levels of nutrient supply and critically low levels. Growers who use fertilizers in the plantation must be aware of the potential for nutrient interactions, trying to take advantage of the positive ones while avoiding the negative.

12.0 POTENTIAL FERTILIZER RESPONSES FOR IMPORTANT CHRISTMAS TREE SPECIES

In the natural environment, conifers grow on a wide range of sites. Some species are especially well-adapted to poor, dry soils on highly exposed sites, while others prefer better conditions. Even within a species there is often tremendous variation in site tolerances and preferences. Scots pine is a good example. It ranges widely across northern and central Europe where mountains and large bodies of water limit the movement of genetic information, resulting in the formation of distinct strains. These strains are classified together as a single species because they have the same floristic characteristics. However, their growth form, foliage color and site tolerances are often very different. These differences are known as "ecotypic variation." Sometimes even variation within a strain is tremendous; so much so that offspring from the same population will react differently to similar circumstances. Natural genetic variability can cause vast differences in response to uniform treatments, which is another reason why generic fertilizer prescriptions are often ineffective.

Generally, those species and strains that can survive on harsh sites do not respond to fertilizers as readily as trees that are adapted to better sites. Poor-site trees are adapted to infertile soils with mechanisms that increase their uptake capacity for scarce elements (25). A much greater root growth capacity is one such mechanism. However, these species usually exhibit slower top growth, regardless of soil conditions, than species adapted to better sites.

Fertilizers applied to trees that are adapted to nutrient-poor conditions are often wasted. Even though trees may absorb the nutrients, enhanced fertility often will not improve growth, color, bud formation or any characteristic of importance to the grower. Notwithstanding, there are instances where conifers not known to respond to fertilizers, do show a response. A fertilizer trial in the plantation is often the only way to determine if a response is possible.

Successful use of fertilizers must encompass knowledge about the biological capacity of species in the plantation. The purpose of this section is to describe the nutrient demands and site tolerances of some of the commercially important Christmas tree species in North America. Table 12-1 lists these species according to their relative site demands.

TABLE 12-1 The relative nutrient demands of important Christmas tree species. Those species with higher demands are more apt to respond to soil amendments.

Not Demanding	Moderate Demands	Demanding
Scots pine	Norway spruce	Douglas fir
Virginia pine	Balsam fir	Blue spruce
	Fraser fir	White pine
	White spruce	
	Red pine	

12.1 Scots pine

The most commercially important strains of Scots pine grown in North America come from the region of Southern France and Spain. Growers prefer these strains because the foliage retains its green color year-round and they can be planted with good success on even the poorest sites. Other strains from Northern and Eastern Europe tend to turn slightly yellow in the fall making their use for Christmas trees impractical. The yellowing is a genetic trait that cannot be overcome with fertilizers. Foliage tinting with green dye at harvest time is a standard practice in some areas to hide off-color foliage.

Another cause of yellowing in Scots pine results from an interaction with the site. Most strains will exhibit light green or yellow-green foliage when grown on inadequately drained, clay soils. This effect cannot be overcome with fertilizers.

Spanish strains of Scots pine planted in North America grow best when fertility is low (9). "Low" is defined as 10 ppm N, 5 ppm P, and 10 ppm K. In contrast, German and Swedish strains will respond to fertilizers applied at a moderate rate ("moderate" is six times higher than the "low" level). High levels of fertility (11 times higher than the "low" level) caused a decrease in growth rate of the Spanish strains.

In another experiment, fertilizer treatments at the time of planting had no effect on Scots pine even after four years (43). Other investigators have reported similar results (7, 35).

Scots pine prefers an acid soil. It exhibits maximum growth at a soil-in-water pH of 5.0 (12). Growth rate declines rapidly as pH is increased to 6.0.

Virginia pine, grown for Christmas trees in the Southeast U.S., is somewhat similar to Scots pine. It prefers a pH within the range of 5.0–5.5. However, it may be more responsive to fertilizer treatments in some circumstances than Scots pine. In one study, fertilizers applied to newly planted Virginia pine where herbicides have been used to control weeds caused more mortality than where weeds were controlled by mowing (62).

Growers who use fertilizers with these species should do so sparingly. High rates are known to cause more harm than good and it is hard to justify the labor and material expense for applications that yield little or no response. Scots pine does respond to favorable moisture conditions, so a suspected response to fertilizer should not be confused with the effect of adequate rainfall throughout the growing season. Also, Scots pine should not be planted in clay soils or on any other sites with restricted drainage.

12.2 Balsam fir, Fraser fir and white spruce

These species, all natives of North America, have moderate nutrient demands. They occur on a wide range of sites and do very well on good sites. Fertilizer responses are best when these species are planted on nutrient-poor soils.

Balsam and Fraser fir are close relatives. So close, in fact that Fraser fir could be considered a southern variant of balsam. They have very similar growth form, foliage and needle color. When planted together in the same plantation they are often difficult to distinguish. Although a number of fertilizer studies have been reported for balsam fir, there is little applicable published research on Fraser fir. However, since the species are so similar, the results of balsam studies are probably applicable to Fraser. The optimum soil-in-water pH for these species is within the range of 5.5–6.0.

Faster growth, longer needles, and more and larger buds in the year after treatment, are attributable to fertilizer applications in balsam fir plantations (16, 29, 33, 53, 54). In the Canadian Maritimes, ammonium nitrate (34-0-0) applied at a rate of 165–275 lbs. (56–94 lbs. of elemental N) per acre is considered optimum. Needle lengths can be increased by 1–5 mm from this application and foliage density increased by 10-20% (16). These same stands did not respond to applications of P and K.

An application of 2 ounces per tree of 7-40-6, banded in the root zone two years after planting balsam fir on loam and sandy loam soils, substantially reduced winter burning while improving needle color and increasing needle length (29). Subsurface banding in this experiment provided substantially better results than a surface application of 10-10-10.

. A high rate of application of 152 lbs. of elemental N per acre as ammonium nitrate increased foliar N levels from 1.2%–1.8% and substantially improved needle color and size (33). The number of internodal buds and branches, however, was correlated with foliar concentrations of N, P, K and Mg, not just N.

In other studies with balsam fir, an application of 2 oz. of elemental N per tree increased needle weights by 25%–38%. Once again, P and K applications had no effect on needle weights. However, when P was applied with N, there was an increase in bud development (53, 54). The number of needles, and the number of terminal and lateral buds increased in the second year following fertilization.

For Canadian Maritime plantations of balsam fir, one researcher suggests no fertilizer applications in the year of planting (17). In the following spring, two light applications of N, spaced about 6 weeks apart, that provide a total of 50–60 lbs. elemental N per acre, gave better results than a single heavy application.

In one of the few good studies of the effects of fertilizers on Christmas trees, Bruns (10) suggests that applications every other year of N,P,K at rates of 1.6 oz. N, 1.8 oz. P and 1.9 oz. K per 4–5 foot tall balsam fir tree will improve color, increase leader growth and increase the number of internodal buds and branches in New Hampshire. Annual fertilizer applications did not substantially improve nutrition over applications ever second year.

White spruce has a fairly wide site tolerance. It will survive on extremely poor soils, but like balsam and Fraser fir, it does very well on good sites. Norway spruce, an associate of Scots pine in Europe, is very similar to white spruce. Although not grown as commonly for Christmas trees, Norway spruce has been the subject of many fertilizer experiments, the results of which are probably applicable to white spruce.

In a fertilizer experiment that included white spruce, Stephens and Jaynes (50) reported that the most cost effective treatment was liming. A fairly high pH of 6.5 was identified by the authors as optimum. Most other research suggests that a pH of 6.5 is too high for most Christmas tree species, with the exception of red cedar that does well on nearly neutral soils. The researchers also do not advocate fertilizer applications at the time of establishment, citing the potential for more harm than good.

In Sweden, Norway spruce is considered to be intermediate in nutrient demands, with a slightly higher need for P than is required by pine (26). However, adequate levels of K were associated with better water economy and improved winter survival. The ammonium ion (NH4) was also found to be a much more important source of N than nitrate. Another study reported that applications of Ca and P, alone and in combination with N, increased the growth rate of planted Norway spruce (23). However, if N is in short supply, spruce will uptake luxury quantities of P and K (27).

A single application of about 4.5 oz. of superphosphate (0-20-0) per Norway spruce seedling at the time of planting was found to last for 10 years (19). Liming can prolong the effect for up to 20 years. Meagher and Armson (39) discovered that mixing phosphate with the soil at one inch below the surface had a greater effect on the growth of white spruce seedlings than surface applications. Phosphorus does not move appreciably in the soil so mixing will improve availability unless the soil is strongly acid.

In another experiment, white spruce seedlings fertilized with 100 lbs. of elemental N and 50 lbs. of elemental P per acre grew well throughout the growing season while unfertilized trees grew for only about two-thirds of the growing season (3).

In Europe, Christmas tree growers are advised to apply P and K prior to planting Norway spruce, mixing it with the soil if possible (5). Phosphate (P_2O_5) at a rate 90 lbs. per acre, and potash (K_2O) at 110–160 lbs. per acre are recommended. After planting, 9–36 lbs. per acre of elemental N can be applied as a topdress. They also recommend doubling the rate of N application in the year of harvest.

12.3 Douglas-fir, blue spruce, white pine and red pine

These North American species have fairly high nutrient demands. They will not do well on excessively acid (pH less than 4.5) and nutrient poor sites. The optimum soil-in-water pH is within the range of 5.5–6.0. These species should not be planted on sandy, dry soils because it is too difficult to overcome the negative effects of a poor site with soil amendments.

Douglas-fir has been the subject of many fertilizer studies because it is an important timber species in the Northwestern U.S. and Canada. It is not a true fir. Rather, botanists classify it in a genus by itself. It ranges across Western North America and, like Scots pine, there are many distinct strains. Within its range, Douglas-fir is usually found on the best sites, often growing in association with blue spruce. It will not tolerate wet or imperfectly drained sites.

When planted on soils having a soil-in-water pH lower than 5.5, Douglas-fir and blue spruce will respond to applications of limestone (21, 50). In fact, one study reported that a limestone application was a more effective treatment than applications of N,P,K (50).

In another study, 200 lbs. per acre of elemental N broadcast on three-year old Douglas-fir plantation resulted in significant increases in stem diameter and tree weights (58).

In a fertilizer study using Douglas-fir Christmas trees, applications of 2.0–4.0 ounces of elemental N per 15 foot tree dramatically improved color in a single growing season (57). Rates higher than 2.0 ounces caused over-stimulation. The color change was tied exclusively to N content of foliage. Phosphorus and K had no effect of foliage color. However, complete fertilization (N, P, K, S & Mg) resulted in cone formation. Phosphorus and K rates were on the order of 1.6 oz. elemental P and 3.2 oz. elemental K per tree. This same study recommends that elemental N application rates be kept under 2.0 ounces per tree to avoid over-stimulation, except in the year of harvest when up to 4.0 ounces can be applied to improve color.

Some researchers advise that high rates of phosphate should not be used on conifers (22). Applications of 268 lbs. of elemental P per acre raised foliar P levels but reduced foliar N. However, good response to P appeared to be tied to adequate supplies of N. When N was lacking, the response to P applications was limited. The authors suggest that available-P soil test values of less than 4 lbs. per acre will result in P deficiencies in Douglas- fir.

In another experiment, P applications had no effect on the growth of Douglas-fir seedlings, but survival was improved (61). Nitrogen applied at elemental rates of 0.3–0.6 ounces per seedling at the time of planting increased height growth by 12–31% after three to six years. Increased growth rate in this instance was tied solely to N applications.

Another researcher reported that an application of ammonium phosphate (16-20-0) at a rate of 5.0 oz. of fertilizer per 7- year-old tree yielded the best height growth response in Douglas-fir (30).

Eastern white pine is a fairly common species in the Northeast and Northcentral states. Red pine is a common associate in the north. Neither species has been the subject of many fertilizer studies except those that relate to nursery practice. Of the two species, white pine is used more commonly for Christmas trees, but in some northern states, red pine is grown as well. The optimum soil-in-water pH for these species is within the range of 5.0–5.5.

White pine Christmas trees in Virginia, 7–9 years old, that had been severely injured by ozone and sulfur dioxide air pollution responded dramatically to topdressed applications of 25-9-9 at rates of 8 to 24 oz. of fertilizer per tree (64). These treatments had a substantial effect lowering the incidence of "tip-burn" from pollution and changing tree colors from yellow green to dark green. To help alleviate the effects of air pollutants on white pine foliage, the authors suggest the following guidelines: using 25-9-9 fertilizer, for trees 1–3 feet in height, 8 oz. per tree; for trees 3–6 feet, 16 oz.; and for trees over 6 feet, 24–32 oz. of fertilizer per tree.

In a more recent study of the use of fertilizers on white pine grown for Christmas trees, researchers reported that after 4 years white pine height growth was improved by complete fertilizer applications at the time of planting (43). The most effective treatment was 0.5–1.0 oz. of 20-10-10 fertilizer applied to the soil surface after planting. However, the author notes that vigor and color ratings in white pine were not affected by fertilizer treatments.

Both white pine and red pine have a high uptake capacity for N,P and K (28). However, red pine has a slightly higher uptake capacity than white pine for K. This means that high application rates are not necessary to ensure that these trees obtain adequate nutrition. It also means that both species may consume luxury quantities of nutrients without corresponding changes in growth.

12.4 Summary

Species like Scots pine that have only slight nutrient demands will not usually respond to fertilizer treatments that are intended to increase growth rate, improve color or stimulate bud formation. However, in some circumstances trees may respond. Unless soil test values are extremely low, the use of fertilizers with these species should be considered experimental. Growers should not confuse a response due to other environmental factors, such as increased rainfall, when fertilizers are used. A suitable objective in plantations of these species may be to build fertility on the site in anticipation of replanting to a more demanding species in the next rotation.

When soil pH is too high (> 5.5) for acid-tolerant species like Scots pine and Virginia pine, trees will not do well and the effect cannot be overcome with fertilizers. The only way to prepare these sites for Christmas trees is to lower soil pH with applications of acidifying agents like sulfur (see section 9.4).

Species with moderate and high nutrient demands will usually respond to light applications of N—0.25–0.5 oz. of elemental N per tree, every other year, in the first few years, increasing up to 1.0–2.0 ounces as trees get larger. If leader lengths become excessive, such that they are spindly and twisted, the rate should be decreased. With the exception of phosphate, fertilizer applications at the time of planting should be avoided unless the foliar nutrient levels of seedlings are extremely low (see section 8.2), or the rates of application are kept very low. Surface applications should kept away from the seedling stems. Three to 4.0 ounces of elemental N per tree can be applied in the year of harvest to produce dark green foliage. However, if tree color is already acceptable with the lower dose, there is no need to increase the rate for a very slight improvement in color.

When required, phosphate should be applied subsurface, either as a band to avoid mixing in soils that are strongly acid (pH of 4.5 or less and high levels of aluminum or iron), or otherwise mixed well with the soil. On sandy soils that have a low cation exchange capacity surface applications are acceptable, especially when concentrated and highly soluble forms of phosphate, like triple superphosphate (0-46-0), are used.

Ordinary superphosphate (0-20-0) can be used at rates up to about 4.0 ounces of fertilizer per seedling, or triple superphosphate (0-46-0) at rates up to 2.0 ounces per seedling. Seedling roots should not come into contact with phosphate granules, especially when 0-46-0 is used. When phosphate is applied as a band, it should be placed at least two inches away from the roots, either below or to the side. This will allow the roots to grow into the band.

Surface applications of phosphate on fine soils, particularly on sloping ground subject to runoff, should be avoided. Sandy soils with a low cation exchange capacity are an exception to this rule. Another exception is when ammonium phosphates are used. These materials can be applied to the surface with good effect when the rates are kept low and soils have been limed to the proper pH.

Potassium may not be required at all during the rotation unless soil test values are low—less than 100 lbs. per acre. When needed, K can be applied as a topdressing at least six inches away from the base of the tree. Rates of application should be kept low to avoid antagonism with other elements.

If soil pH is maintained within the range of 5.0–6.0 (soil-in-water method) an application of micronutrients will probably not be required.

13.0 USING FERTILIZERS IN THE PLANTATION

Fertilizers play an important role in the culture of Christmas trees. Properly used, they can improve the color and quality of trees, help protect them during times of adversity, and even shorten the rotation. However, when used indiscriminately, fertilizers can be expensive and sometimes damaging to trees, and they can also be a potential source of water pollution.

This last section looks at the economics of using fertilizers in the plantation. Also discussed are proper storage and handling requirements for fertilizers, and how to avoid polluting water supplies.

13.1 The Economics of Fertilizer Use

According to one of the few studies that have looked at the economics of using fertilizers in the Christmas tree plantation, the species that are most apt to benefit from fertilization are Douglas-fir, the spruces, the true firs and eastern white pine (35). Most improvement with these species is seen when fertilizers are used to supplement fertility of inherently poor and sandy soils. In these instances fertilization can result in a 2–4% return on investment. However, by shortening the rotation even one year, the return on investment may be as high as 10% or more.

The costs of fertilization usually include machine, labor and material costs. Of the three, material costs are the most expensive and the most difficult to estimate. The cost of fertilizer materials are variable and depend on such factors as nutrient concentration and the quantity purchased. Cost per unit of nutrient usually decreases with concentration. All other things being equal, urea (46-0-0) is usually a cheaper source of N than ammonium nitrate (34-0-0), but not always. Since one of the major costs of fertilizer production is transportation, a more local source of ammonium nitrate may be more cost effective than urea or any other source of N. It usually pays to ask local fertilizer dealers about the unit costs of different nutrient sources before putting in an order.

Machine costs attributable to the application of fertilizers may range from $1.00 to $20.00 per acre per year or more depending upon the level of mechanization. This includes both fixed and variable costs attributable to those hours machines like tractors, trailers and spreaders, are devoted to transporting or applying fertilizers in the plantation. Using machines to apply fertilizers can result in substantial labor savings, but material costs are usually higher than when fertilizers are applied by hand.

Labor costs include handling and transporting fertilizers and applying them around the base of individual trees. Time devoted to fertilization varies with the amount of fertilizer placed around each tree. Growers should be able to treat, by hand, 100–360 trees per hour (35). With 1,200 trees per acre, that is 3.3 to 12 hours per acre per application. A labor rate of 1.5–2.5 hours to fertilize 1,350 Douglas firs per acre has been reported for western Washington (11).

The annual cost of fertilization, including machine costs, materials and labor, should be within the range of $0.05 to $0.15 per tree. As a general rule, the total cost of fertilization should not exceed 12% of the selling price of standing trees. In the Washington study cited above, the cost of fertilization was about 3% of the selling price of trees before harvest (11).

Growers who consistently use complete fertilizers when only one or two elements are necessary are substantially increasing the cost of fertilization and decreasing profitability. For example, a grower who uses 10-10-10 to supply one ounce of N per tree will pay 3–4 times more per unit of N than if ammonium nitrate is used. If N is the only element lacking, the extra cost for P and K is unwarranted. On the other hand, if N and K are limiting a balanced fertilizer containing N,P and K may cost little more than N and K alone. The additional P can be a bonus. Nitrogen is usually the most costly element in a complete fertilizer.

The grower must also consider the time-value of money invested in soil amendments. Ten cents per tree spent on fertilization at the time of establishment should be worth about 20 cents ten years hence, when the compound interest rate is 7.2%. This analysis assumes that the grower could have invested the ten cents in some other alternative and earned

7.2% interest on it:

$$\$0.10 \times (1 + 0.072)^{10} = \$0.20$$

(0.072 is the interest rate. A grower may choose a different rate if it is a better approximation of the cost of foregoing another opportunity in favor of fertilizing trees.)

From the grower's perspective, the longer an investment must be maintained, the more expensive it is. In practical terms this means that lavish and costly treatments at the time of plantation establishment may not be as cost effective as more conservative treatments spread over a number of years. Considering the example above, if the grower had spent only five cents per tree at establishment and ten cents per tree at 5 years into a 10 year rotation, the sum of the future value of these two investments, compounded annually at 7.2%, is 24 cents, only slightly more than the value of a single treatment costing 10 cents but carried for a longer period. On the basis of this example, it should be clear that fertilizer treatments intended to improve tree color are most cost-effective when employed later in the rotation. The grower must also remember that some sites and some species do not require any supplementary fertilization.

Another point to keep in mind is this: even with species and sites that will respond to fertilizers, annual applications are rarely required. Also, the cost of fertilization during the rotation can be treated for tax purposes as an expense of the business. The cost of fertilization at the time of planting, however, must be added to the cost basis of trees and recovered when the trees are sold.

13.2 Fertilizer Storage and Handling

Growers who are able to store fertilizers at the plantation will be able to take advantage of discounts on bulk purchases. However, proper storage facilities are a necessary prerequisite.

Commercial fertilizers are manufactured as salts. Salts attract water to varying degrees, so in wet or humid environments fertilizers will cake, or begin to dissolve and dissociate. For this reason, fertilizers should be stored in a dry, well-ventilated space.

Some fertilizers are classified as hazardous materials. Two very common ones are ammonium nitrate and potassium nitrate. Both are oxidizing agents, which means that if conditions are right they will burn fiercely. If contaminated with oil or some other source of carbon, ammonium nitrate is explosive. Both of these fertilizers should be stored off the floor in a well-ventilated shed away from power equipment. Buildings with floor drains should be avoided to prevent flushing of these chemicals into the environment in case of fire. Storage buildings should be located as far as possible from wells and surface waters to eliminate the potential for accidental contamination.

Materials such as lime, urea, ammonium sulfate, superphosphate, diammonium phosphate, and potash are not classified as hazardous materials (63). However, fertilizers do produce dust and anything over 15 mg. / cu. meter is considered hazardous by the Occupational Safety and Health Administration (OSHA), (63). A particle mask while loading equipment hoppers is usually necessary. Gloves will help protect the skin from the desiccating effects of salts when fertilizers must be handled for extended periods.

13.2.1 Applying Fertilizers With Machines

There are a few pieces of commercially available equipment to help growers with the application of fertilizers . The important thing to remember is that equipment decisions need to be made before the plantation is established. It is much more difficult to locate suitable equipment after the trees are planted. Many growers have found themselves with expensive equipment that is almost useless because it no longer fits between tree rows.

Broadcast spreaders that throw fertilizer granules through the trees have been used successfully in plantations designed to accommodate this technology. However, many growers are not willing to sacrifice so much space to roads and would rather fertilize by hand. Hand applications are much more efficient than machine spreading in young plantations. But later in the rotation after roots have spread between tree rows, mechanized broadcast applications are usually more efficient, especially in large plantations.

Figure 13-1. Broadcast spreaders can be used to good effect in older plantations that have been properly designed to accommodate this equipment. By permission of VICON, Inc.

The high initial cost of mechanization is usually difficult for most small-scale growers to justify. Nevertheless, small-ness has not prevented the construction of homespun equipment and tools to help with the job of applying fertilizers. Some of this equipment is quite ingenious. One such device is based on a concept that is similar to that employed in shotgun shell loaders: Attached to the bottom of a backpack used for carrying fertilizers is a gate-valve and hand lever. The gate-valve allows a hollow cylinder of known volume to fill with fertilizer. When the grower pulls down on the lever the gate-valve is closed and a measured dose of fertilizer is

Figure 13-2. A back pack fertilizer system made by I.R.S., Inc. (Address listed in Appendix D.)

sent down a section of flexible hose that is directed around the drip line of the tree. Equipment that employs a similar concept is now commercially available (Figure 13-2).

For many growers, the most cost effective method of applying fertilizers is by hand. However, as the operation grows, most will discover ways to mechanize since machine costs are usually much cheaper than labor. Growers who have had equipment successes are usually anxious to share their inventions with others. Local, regional and national Christmas tree grower association newsletters and meetings will often feature the technological innovations of its members.

13.2.2 Measuring Fertilizer Amounts

Fertilizer recommendations are often given on the basis of weight, yet most growers do not have the equipment to weigh fertilizers. Also, when a prescription calls for 2 oz. of ordinary superphosphate per tree, taking the time to weigh an equivalent amount for each tree is impractical. The easiest method of measuring fertilizer amounts by hand is to convert fertilizer weights into equivalent volumes. Doing so enables the grower to fabricate a scoop that provides the proper dose. An ordinary juice can, preferably with non-metallic sides, will make an excellent scoop.

Table 13-1 lists the bulk density of some common fertilizer materials, and Table 13-2 show the cubic volume per inch of height for two common juice can sizes. To calculate the cubic volume of other size cans, see Appendix D.

TABLE 13-1 The mean bulk density, or weight per unit volume, of selected fertilizer materials in ounces per cubic inch. Adapted from the Farm Chemical Handbook, 1988 (18).

Material	Bulk Density (oz. / cu. in.)
Ammonium nitrate (granular)	0.5
Ammonium nitrate (prilled)	0.55
Ammonium sulfate	0.5
Urea (crystal)	0.33
Urea (pellet)	0.38
Urea-form	0.26
Monoammonium phosphate	0.5
Diammonium phosphate	0.42
Ordinary superphosphate	0.53
Triple superphosphate	0.56
Potassium nitrate	0.60
N-K mixed fertilizer	0.54
N-P-K mixed fertilizer	0.56
P-K mixed fertilizer	0.62
Dolomite	0.89
Limestone (fine)	0.93
Manure (sheep & cattle, dry)	0.23

TABLE 13-2 Cubic inches of volume per inch in height for two common juice can sizes.

Can size	Cubic inches per inch in can height
Small (6 fl. ozs. - diameter = 2.06 inches)	3.33
Large (12 or 16 fl. ozs. - diameter = 2.56 in.)	5.14

To use the juice cans listed in Table 13-2, figure the equivalent volume for the recommended weight of the material in question using Table 13-1, then divide this figure by the appropriate value from Table 13-2. For example, to apply 3 oz. of triple superphosphate using a small juice can, divide 3 oz. by 0.56—the equivalent volume of 1 oz. of triple. Divide the answer by the volume for the appropriate can size. The result is the can height that will provide a measured dose. In this example, a 2 inch can should be cut to 1.6 inches to make a scoop that supplies 3 oz. of triple superphosphate.

13.3 Protecting Water Supplies

When soil amendments move from the site into surface and ground water supplies, water quality usually suffers. Nitrogen and phosphorus are the two principal culprits. Although Christmas tree plantations are better at conserving fertilizers than most cultivated fields, one must consider the sobering fact that losses of plant nutrients from farm and forest lands during the past fifty years in the U.S., due to erosion and runoff, have exceeded nutrient removals by crops (63).

As discussed previously, nitrate-nitrogen (NO_3) leaches readily through virtually all mineral soils and will reach the water table with percolating rainfall. Losses of NO_3 to groundwater are usually only a small percentage of what is applied to cultivated fields. This figure should be considerably less in Christmas tree plantations because application rates are usually only a fraction of those applied to field crops. However, when high N-application rates are followed by excessive rainfall, there is the potential of increasing groundwater-N above levels deemed safe for human consumption.

The U.S. Public Health Service has determined that 10 ppm N, or 45 ppm NO_3, in drinking water is the threshold above which health hazards are possible (63). High nitrate levels in drinking water can lead to methemoglobinemia, a diminished capacity of blood to transport oxygen. Oxygen starvation, especially among infants, leads to a bluish discoloration of tissues, hence the name "blue baby disease". Fortunately, the occurrence of blue baby disease is very rare. However, wells which tap into an aquifer that extends below nearby plantations where high rates of fertilizers have been used should be tested periodically, especially in early summer when nitrate levels are apt to be highest.

One way to avoid the possibility of nitrate pollution is to apply less N, but more often. Single heavy doses, particularly on well-drained, sandy soils, are more apt to cause problems than lighter applications spread over a longer period. Also, efficiency of use is much higher with lighter applications. Ammonium sources are less apt to cause nitrate pollution. However, in warm soils ammonium will be mineralized to nitrate in due time.

Since most N sources dissolve quickly when it rains and move readily into the soil, pollution of surface waters from runoff is not usually a problem. However, high rates of application on sloping sites that have imperfectly drained soils, followed by rains heavy enough to cause overland flow, can lead to problems. Nitrogen in surface waters will stimulate algae growth.

Phosphorus, though not so much a direct health hazard, can cause pollution of surface waters in the same way. By enriching streams and lakes, P also encourages the growth of algae and bacteria that consume oxygen and destroy habitat for fish and other animals. When P is applied to the soil surface, runoff from heavy rains will transport it to surface waters. Phosphorus does not move appreciably in most soils, it tends to stay where it is put. However, when the site is sloping and unprotected by sod cover, P can be picked up as soil particles to which it is attached go into suspension. The result—P is lost from the site and local surface waters are polluted. As little as 50 parts per billion of phosphorus in surface waters can trigger algae blooms.

To avoid the possibility of losing P, it should be applied below the soil surface. Doing so not only protects it from export, but it also increases efficiency. Maintaining sod cover in the plantation and using untreated buffer strips between fertilized plantations and surface waters will also help minimize pollution risks.

14.0 APPENDIX

GLOSSARY OF TERMS

(The terms defined in this glossary are adapted from the **Western Fertilizer Handbook**, 1990, with the permission of the California Fertilizer Association.)

AAPFCO—American Association of Plant Food Control Officials. An organization that sets standards for commercially available fertilizer materials.

ACID-FORMING—A term applied to any fertilizer that tends to make the soil more acid.

ACID SOIL—A soil with a pH value below 7.0. A soil having a preponderance of hydrogen over hydroxyl ions in the soil solution.

AGGREGATE—A group of soil particles cohering so as to behave mechanically as a unit.

AMENDMENT—Any material, such as fertilizer, lime, gypsum, sawdust or synthetic conditioners, applied to the soil to make it more productive.

AMINO ACIDS—Nitrogen-containing compounds, large numbers of which link together in the formation of the protein molecule. Each amino acid molecule contains one or more amino ($-NH_2$) groups and at least one carboxyl ($-COOH$) group. In addition, some amino acids (cystine and methionine) contain sulfur.

ANION—An ion carrying a negative charge of electricity.

AVAILABLE—In general, a form capable of being assimilated by a growing plant. Available nitrogen is defined as the nitrogen that is water-soluble plus what can be made soluble or converted into free ammonia. Available phosphoric acid is that portion which is water-soluble plus the part which is soluble in ammonium citrate.

AVAILABLE NUTRIENT IN SOIL / MEDIA—The part of the supply of a plant nutrient in the soil that can be taken up by plants at rates and in amounts significant to plant growth.

BASE EXCHANGE—The replacement of cations, held on the soil complex, by other cations. (See also CATION EXCHANGE CAPACITY.)

BUFFER CAPACITY OF SOIL—The ability of the soil to resist a change in its pH (hydrogen ion concentration) when acid-forming or base-forming materials are added to the soil.

BULK DENSITY—The ratio of the mass of water-free soil to its bulk volume. Bulk density is expressed in pounds per cubic foot or grams per cubic centimeter and is sometimes referred to as apparent density. When expressed in grams per cubic centimeter, bulk density is numerically equal to apparent specific gravity or volume weight.

CALCIUM CARBONATE EQUIVALENT—The amount of calcium carbonate required to neutralize acidity produced by a given quantity of fertilizer product.

CARBOHYDRATE—A compound containing carbon, hydrogen and oxygen. Usually the hydrogen and oxygen occur in the proportion of 2 to 1, such as in glucose ($C_6H_{12}O_6$).

CATION—An ion carrying a positive charge of electricity. Common soil cations are calcium, magnesium, sodium, potassium and hydrogen.

CATION EXCHANGE CAPACITY—The total quantity of cations which a soil can adsorb by cation exchange, usually expressed as milliequivalents per 100 grams. Measured values of cation exchange capacity depend somewhat on the method used for the determination. BUFFER CAPACITY is approximately the same measure.

CHELATES—Certain organic chemicals, known as chelating agents, form ring compounds in which a polyvalent metal is held between two or more atoms. Such rings are chelates. Among the best chelating agents known are ethyl-enediaminetetraacetic acid (EDTA), hydroxyethylenedia-minetriacetic acid (HEDTA) and diethylenetria-minepentaacetic acid (DTPA). Citric acid is also used as a chelating agent.

CHLOROSIS—Yellowing of green portions of a plant, particularly the leaves.

CITRATE-SOLUBLE PHOSPHORIC ACID—That fraction of the phosphoric acid insoluble in water but soluble in neutral ammonium citrate. However, since that soluble in water is also soluble in ammonium citrate, "citrate-soluble" may be used to indicate the sum of water-soluble plus citrate soluble phosphoric acid. (See also AVAILABLE.)

CLAY—A minute soil particle less than 0.002 millimeter in diameter and having a predominately negative charge.

COATED FERTILIZERS—Fertilizer materials, generally urea, that are coated to slow the release of the fertilizer. Coating material is most commonly sulfur, but resins and thermoplastics are also used.

COLLOID—The soil particles (inorganic or organic) having small diameters ranging from 0.20 to 0.0005 micron. Colloids are characterized by high base exchange.

COMPLETE FERTILIZER—A fertilizer containing all three of the primary fertilizer nutrients (nitrogen, phosphate and potash) in sufficient amounts to be of value as nutrients.

CONDITIONER (of fertilizer)—A material added to a fertilizer to prevent caking and to keep it free-flowing.

CONDUCTIVITY, ELECTRICAL—A physical quantity that measures the readiness with which a medium transmits electricity. Commonly used for expressing the salinity of irrigation waters and soil extracts because it can be directly related to salt concentration. It is expressed in decisiemens per meter (dS/m), or in millisiemens per centimeter (mS/cm) or millimhos per centimeter (mmhos/cm), at 25 degrees Centigrade.

DENITRIFICATION—The process by which nitrates or nitrites in the soil or organic deposits are reduced to lower oxides of nitrogen by bacterial action. The process results in the escape of nitrogen into the air.

DOLOMITE—A material used for liming soils in areas where magnesium and calcium are needed. Made by grinding dolomitic limestone which contains both magnesium carbonate, $MgCO_3$ and calcium carbonate $CaCO_3$. (See also LIME.)

ENZYMES—Protein substances produced by living cells which can change the rate of chemical reactions. They are organic catalysts.

EROSION—The wearing away of the land surface by detachment and transport of soil and rock materials through the action of moving water, wind or other geological agents.

EXCHANGEABLE IONS—Ions held on the soil complex that may be replace by other ions of like charge. Ions which are held so tightly that they cannot be exchanged are called nonexchangeable.

FERTILIZER—Any natural or manufactured material added to the soil in order to supply one or more plant nutrients. The term is generally applied to largely inorganic materials other than lime or gypsum.

FERTILIZER FORMULA—The quantity and grade of materials used in making a fertilizer mixture.

FERTILIZER RATIO—The relative proportions of primary nutrients in a fertilizer grade divided by the highest divisor for that grade; e.g., grades 10-6-4 and 20-12-8 have the ratio 5-3-2.

FIXATION—The process by which available plant nutrients are rendered unavailable or "fixed" in the soil. Generally, the process by which potassium, phosphorus and ammonium are rendered unavailable in the soil. Also the process by which free nitrogen is chemically combined either naturally or synthetically. (See also NITROGEN FIXATION.)

FOLIAR FERTILIZATION—Supplying plant nutrients through leaves, with absorption taking place through the stomata of leaves and leaf cuticles.

GRADE—The guaranteed analysis of a fertilizer containing one or more of the primary plant nutrient elements. Grades are stated in terms of the guaranteed percentages of nitrogen (N), available phosphate (P_2O_5) and potash (K_2O) in that order. For example, a 10-10-10 grade would contain 10% nitrogen, 10% available phosphate, and 10% potash.

GUARANTEES—The AAPFCO official regulation follows: The statement of guarantees of mixed fertilizer shall be given in whole numbers. All fertilizer components with the exception of potash (K_2O) and phosphoric acid (P_2O_5) if guaranteed, shall be stated in terms of the elements.

GYPSUM—($CaSO_4$-$2H_2O$) The common name for calcium sulfate, a mineral used in the fertilizer industry as a source of calcium and sulfur. Gypsum also is used widely in reclaiming alkali soils in the eastern United States. Gypsum cannot be used as a liming material, but it may reduce the alkalinity of sodic soils by replacing sodium with calcium. Another common name is landplaster. When pure it contains approximately 18.6 percent sulfur.

HYGROSCOPIC—Capable of taking up moisture from the air.

INORGANIC—Substances occurring as minerals in nature or obtainable from them by chemical means. Refers to all matter except the compounds of carbon, but includes carbonates.

INSOLUBLE—Not soluble. As applied to phosphoric acid in fertilizer, that portion of the total phosphoric acid which is soluble neither in water nor in neutral ammonium citrate. As applied to potash and nitrogen, not soluble in water.

ION—An electrically charged particle. As used in soils, an ion refers to an electrically charged element or combination of elements resulting from the breaking up of an electrolyte (salt) in solution. Since most soil solutions are very dilute, many of the salts exist as ions. For example, all or part of the potassium chloride (muriate of potash) in most soils exists as potassium ions and chloride ions. The positively charged potassium ion is a cation, and the negatively charged chloride ion is an anion.

LEACHING—The removal of materials in solution by the passage of water through soil.

LIME—Generally the term lime, or agricultural lime, is applied to ground limestone (calcium carbonate), hydrated lime (calcium hydroxide) or burned lime (calcium oxide) with or without mixtures of magnesium carbonate, magnesium hydroxide or magnesium oxide, and to materials such as basic slag, used as amendments to reduce the acidity of acid soils. In strict chemical terminology, lime refers to calcium oxide (CaO), but by an extension of meaning it is now used for all limestone-derived materials applied to neutralize acid soils.

LIME REQUIREMENT—The amount of standard ground limestone required to bring a 6.6-inch layer of an acre (about 2 million pounds in mineral soils) of acid soil to some specific lesser degree of acidity, usually to slightly or very slightly acid. In common practice, lime requirements are given in tons per acre of nearly pure limestone, ground finely enough so that all of it passes a 10-mesh screen and at least half of it passes a 100-mesh screen.

LIQUID FERTILIZER—A fluid in which the plant nutrients are in true solution.

LOAM—The textural class name for soil having a moderate amount of sand, silt and clay. Loam soils contain 7 to 27 percent clay, 28 to 50 percent silt, and less than 52 percent sand. (In the old literature, especially English literature, the term loam applied to mellow soils rich in organic matter, regardless of the texture. As used in the United States, the term refers only to the relative amounts of sand, silt, and clay; loam soils may or may not be mellow.)

LUXURY CONSUMPTION—The uptake by a plant of an essential nutrient in amounts exceeding what it needs.

MACRONUTRIENTS—Nutrients that plants require in relatively large amounts.

MANURE—Generally, the refuse from stables and barnyards, including both animal excreta and straw or other litter. In some other countries the term manure is used more broadly and includes both farmyard or animal manure and "chemical manures," for which the term fertilizer is nearly always used in the United States.

MICRONUTRIENTS—Nutrients that plants need in only small or trace amounts. Essential micronutrients are boron, chlorine, copper, iron, manganese, molybdenum and zinc.

MULCH—A material applied to the ground to prevent excessive drying of the soil surface, to prevent rapid changes in soil temperature, as a soil amendment, for decorative purposes or to prevent weed growth.

MURIATE OF POTASH—Potassium chloride (KCl).

NITRIFICATION—The formation of nitrates and nitrites from ammonia (or ammonium compounds), as in soils by microorganisms.

NITROGEN FIXATION—Generally, the conversion of free nitrogen to nitrogen compounds. Specifically in soils, the assimilation of free nitrogen from the soil air by soil organisms and the formation of nitrogen compounds that eventually become available to plants. The nitrogen-fixing organisms associated with legumes are called symbiotic; those not definitely associated with the higher plants are non-symbiotic or free-living.

NUTRIENT, PLANT—Any element taken in by a plant which is essential to its growth and which is used by the plant in elaboration of its food and tissue.

ORGANIC—Compounds of carbon other than the inorganic carbonates.

PARTS PER MILLION (ppm)—A notation for indicating small amounts of materials. The expression gives the number of units by weight of the substance per million weight units of another substance, such as oven-dry soil. The term may be used to express the number of weight units of a substance per million weight units of a solution. the approximate weight of soil is 2 million pounds per acre—6 inches. Therefore, ppm x 2 equals pounds per acre—6 inches of soil, or ppm x 4 equals pounds per acre-foot of soil.

PERCOLATION—The downward movement of water through soil.

pH—A numerical designation of acidity and alkalinity as in soils and other biological systems. Technically, pH is the common logarithm of the reciprocal of the hydrogen ion concentration of a solution. A pH of 7.0 indicates precise neutrality; higher values indicate increasing alkalinity, and lower values indicate increasing acidity.

PHOSPHATE—A salt of phosphoric acid made by combining phosphoric acid with ions such as ammonium, calcium, potassium or sodium.

PHOSPHATE ROCK—Phosphate-bearing ore composed largely of tricalcium phosphate. Phosphate rock can be treated with strong acids or heat to make available forms of phosphate.

PHOSPHORIC ACID—A term that refers to the phosphorus content of a fertilizer, expressed as phosphoric acid (P_2O_5). The AAPFCO has adopted as official the following definition: "The term phosphoric acid designates P_2O_5." Phosphoric acid also refers to the acid H_3PO_4.

PHOTOSYNTHESIS—The process by which green plants combine water and carbon dioxide to form carbohydrates under the action of light. Chlorophyll is required for the conversion of light energy into chemical energy.

POTASH—The AAPFCO has adopted as official the following definition: "The term potash designates potassium oxide (K_2O)."

PRODUCTIVITY—In simplest terms, the ability of the soil to produce. It differs from fertility to the extent that a soil may be fertile and yet unable to produce because of other limit factors.

PROTEIN—Any of a group of high-molecular-weight nitrogen- containing compounds that yield amino acids on hydrolysis. protein is a vital part of living matter and is one of the essential food substances of animals.

SALT INDEX—An index used to compare solubilities of chemical compounds. Most nitrogen and potash compounds have high indexes, and phosphate compounds have low indexes. When applied too close to see or on foliage, the compounds with high indexes cause plants to wilt or die.

SALTS—The products, other than water, of the reaction of an acid with a base. Salts commonly found in soils break up into cations (sodium, calcium, etc.) and anions (chloride, sulfate, etc.) when dissolved in water.

SAND—Individual rock or mineral fragments in soils having diameters ranging from 0.05 millimeter to 2.0 millimeters. Usually sand grains consist chiefly of quartz, but they may be of any mineral composition. The textural class name of any soil that contains 85 percent or more sand and not more than 10 percent clay.

SILT—(1) Individual mineral particles of soil that range in diameter between the upper size of clay, 0.002 mm, and the lower size of very fine sand, 0.05 mm. (2) Soil of the textural class silt containing 80 percent or more silt and less than 12 percent clay. (3) Sediments deposited from water in which the individual grains are approximately the size of silt, although the term is sometimes applied loosely to sediments containing considerable sand and clay.

STRUCTURE, SOIL—The physical arrangement of the soil particles.

SUPERPHOSPHATE—The AAPFCO has adopted as official the following definition: "Superphosphate is a product obtained by mixing rock phosphate with either sulfuric acid or phosphoric acid or with both acids. (The grade that shows the available phosphoric acid shall be used as a prefix to the name. Example: 20 percent superphosphate.)"

SUSPENSION FERTILIZER—A fluid containing dissolved and undissolved plant nutrients. The suspension of the undissolved plant nutrients may be inherent to the materials or produced with the aid of a suspending agent of non-fertilizer properties. Mechanical agitation may be necessary in some cases to facilitate uniform suspension of undissolved plant nutrients.

SYMBIOSIS—The living together of two different organisms with a resulting mutual benefit. A common example is the association of rhizobia with legumes; the resulting nitrogen fixation is sometimes called symbiotic nitrogen fixation. Adjective: symbiotic.

TEXTURE, SOIL—The relative proportions of the various size groups of individual soil grains in a mass of soil/media. Specifically, it refers to the proportions sand, silt and clay.

TRACE ELEMENTS—See MICRONUTRIENTS

TRANSPIRATION—Loss of water vapor from the leaves and stems of living plants to the atmosphere.

TRIPLE SUPERPHOSPHATE—A product that contains 40 to 50 percent available phosphoric acid. Triple superphosphate differs from ordinary superphosphate.

APPENDIX B

USEFUL CALCULATIONS, MEASURE EQUIVALENTS AND CONVERSIONS

Calculations:

1) To determine the number of trees per acre based on a rectangular spacing pattern . . .

Multiple distance between stems within a row by the distance between rows. Divide the result into 43,560 sq. ft. per acre to obtain number of trees per acre.

Trees planted on a 6 by 6 foot spacing will result in:

6 * 6 = 36 sq. ft.   43,560/36 = 1,210 trees per acre

■ ■

2) To determine the area to be fertilized around the base of a tree . . .

Figure the area of a circle with the stem in the center and the radius equal to the distance from the stem to slightly beyond the extent of the tree's branches:

Area of a circle (sq. ft.) = 3.14 * (radius * radius)

A circle with a radius of 3 feet encompasses:

3.14 * (3 * 3) = 28.3 sq. ft.

■ ■

3) To determine the portion of an acre fertilized when individual trees are treated . . .

Multiple the number of trees per acre by the number of sq. ft. around each tree. The result divided by 43,560 sq. ft. per acre is the portion of an acre treated with fertilizers.

Recommendations provided to the grower on a per-acre basis should be reduced accordingly.

Example: When there are 1,210 tree per acre (6 by 6 ft.) and 28.3 sq. ft. are to be treated around each tree, the total treatment area is:

$$1,210 * 28.3 \text{ sq. ft.} = 34,243 \text{ sq. ft.}$$

$$34,243 \text{ sq. ft.} / 43,560 \text{ sq. ft. per acre} = 0.786$$

Per acre application rates should be reduced by 21.4%

■ ■

4) To convert a recommendation given in lbs. per acre to equivalent weights per tree . . .

First, figure the portion of an acre that is to be treated and reduce per acre figures accordingly.

Divide the result by the number of trees per acre to obtain application rates per tree.

■ ■

5) To find the volume of a can or other cylinder:

$$3.14 \text{ (pi)} \times \text{radius}^2 \times \text{height} = \text{volume}$$

■■

6) To calculate the equivalent volume of a weight of fertilizer, consider the following example:

If a can has a diameter of 2.0 inches, how tall should it be to make a scoop that provides 4.0 ounces of N-P-K mixed fertilizer?

Using Table 13-1, the equivalent volume of 4.0 oz. of an N-P-K mix is calculated as follows:

4.0 oz. / 0.56 oz./cu in = 7.14 cubic inches

Using Table 13-2 to obtain the volume per inch in height of a 2 inch can, how tall should the can be to encompass 7.14 cu. inches?:

7.14 cu. in. / 3.14 cu. in. per inch = 2.3 inches

■■

MEASURES:

Length and Area (English and Metric)

1 acre (ac.)	=	43,560 sq. ft.
1 ac.	=	0.405 hectare (ha.)
1 ha.	=	2.471 ac.
1 inch (in.)	=	2.54 centimeters (cm.)
1 cm.	=	0.3937 in.
1 sq. ft.	=	144 sq. in.

Weight (Avoirdupois and Metric)

1 ton (t.)	=	2,000 pounds (lb.)
1 t.	=	0.9072 metric tons (mt.)
1 lb.	=	0.4536 kilograms (kg.)
1 mt.	=	1,000 kg.
1 kg.	=	2.205 lb.
1 lb.	=	16 ounces (oz.)
1 oz.	=	28.35 grams (g.)
1 g.	=	0.03527 oz.

Volume (English and Metric)

1 tablespoon (tbsp.)	=	3 teaspoons (tsp.)
2 tbsp.	=	1 fluid ounce (fl. oz.)
1 cup (c.)	=	8 fl. oz.
1 pint (pt.)	=	16 fl. oz.
1 quart (qt.)	=	32 fl. oz.
1 gallon (gal.)	=	128 fl. oz.
1 milliliter (mL.)	=	1 cubic centimeter (cu. cm.)
1 liter (L.)	=	1,000 mL.

CONVERSIONS:

1 lb./ac.	=	1.121 kg./ha.
1 kg./ha.	=	0.892 lb./ac
1 part per million (ppm.)	=	2.0 lb./ac. (approx.)

APPENDIX C

LITERATURE CITED

1) Adams, M. B. and H. L. Allen. 1985. Nutrient proportions in foliage of semi-mature loblolly pine. Plant and Soil 86 (1): 2786(1): 27- 34.

2) Armson, K. A. 1959. The use of farmyard manure in forest tree nurseries. For. Chron. 35(2): 100-103.

3) Armson, K. A. 1966. Growth and absorption of nutrients by fertilized and unfertilized white spruce seedlings. For. Chron. 42(2): 127-136.

4) Aronsson, A. 1985. Indications of stress from unbalanced nutrient contents in spruce and pine. For. Absts. 1985 46(6) entry no. 3276.

5) Baule, H. and C. Fricker. 1970. The fertilizer treatment of forest trees. Transl. C.L. Whittles. BLV. 259 p.

6) Bialy, K. 1983. Effect of mineral fertilizers on branching in Scots pine. For. Absts. 1985 46(6) entry no. 3153.

7) Bickelhaupt, D. H., et. al. 1986. Christmas tree fertilization. Conservation Circ. 24 (1). NY State Cooperative Extension Service.

8) Black, C.A. 1968. Soil-plant relationships. John Wiley & Sons, Inc. NY. 792 p.

9) Brown, J. H. 1970. Seedling growth of three Scots pine provenances with varying moisture and fertility treatments. For. Sci. 16: 43-45.

10) Bruns, P. E. 1973. Cultural practices, fertilizing and foliar analysis of balsam fir Christmas trees. NH Ag. Exp. Stat. Bull. No. 501. 30 p.

11) Carkner, R. W. and J. Buhaly. 1982. Christmas tree establishment and production costs and returns, western Washington. Wash. State Univ. Bull. No. 1151.

12) Carter, M. R. 1987. Seedling growth and mineral nutrition of Scots pine under acidic to calcareous soil conditions. Soil Sci. 144 (3): 175-180.

13) Cole, D. W. 1979. Mineral cycling in forest ecosystems of the Pacific Northwest. In: Proc. Forest Fertilization Conf., Univ. of Wash., Instit. of For. Res. Contribution No 40. pp. 29–36.

14) Czapowskyz, M. M., et. al. 1980. Foliar nutrient status of young red spruce and balsam fir in a fertilized stand. U.S. Forest Service Res. Pap. NE-467.

15) Dangerfield, J. and H. Brix. 1979. Comparative effects of ammonium nitrate and urea fertilizers on tree growth and soil processes. In: Proc. Forest Fertilization Conf., Univ. of Wash., Instit. of For. Res. Cont. No. 40. pp. 133–149.

16) Embree, D. G. and G. F. Estabrooks. 1981. Fertilizing balsam fir Christmas trees in wild stands. Canadian Forestry Serv. Tech. Note No. 25.

17) Estabrooks, G. F. 1988. Growing balsam fir Christmas trees in field and forest. Canadian Forestry Service (Maritimes) Information Report M-X-164. 23 p.

18) Farm Chemical Handbook. 1988. Published by the Farm Chemical Handbook, 37841 Euclid Ave., Willoughby, OH 47094.

19) Fiedler, H. J., et. al. 1983. Fertilization with phosphorus and nitrogen in young spruce stands (*Picea abies*). Fertilizer Research 4(2): 155-164.

20) Finck, A. 1982. Fertilizers and fertilization—introduction and practical guide to crop fertilization. Verlag Chemie, Weinheim, W. Germany. 438 p.

21) Heilman, P. and G. Ekuan. 1973. Response of Douglas-fir and western hemlock seedlings to lime. For. Sci. 19(3): 220-224.

22) ibid. 1980. Effects of phosphorus on growth and mycorrhizal development of Douglas-fir. Soil Sci. Soc. Am. J. 44(1): 115–119.

23) Hunger, W. 1986. Soil condition, nutrition and growth performance of Norway spruce (*Picea abies*) in fast growing plantations. Fertilizer Research 10: 243-250.

24) Ingestad, T. 1967. Methods for uniform optimum fertilization of forest tree plants. Proc. I.U.F.R.O. Congress, Munich. Vol. 3: 265–269.

25) ibid. 1974. Towards optimum fertilization. Ambio 3: 49–54.

26) ibid. 1979. Mineral nutritional requirements of Pinus sylvestris and Picea abies. Physiol. Plant. 45: 373–380.

27) Ingestad, T. and M. Kahr. 1985. Nutrition and growth of coniferous seedlings (*Pinus sylvestris, P. contorta* and *Picea abies*) at varied relative nitrogen addition rates. Physiologia Planatarum 65(2): 109-116.

28) Iyer, J. G., et. al. 1989. Plant nutrients removed by nursery stock. USDA Forest Service, Tree Planter's Notes, Vol. 40(2): 8–11.

29) Kinerson, R. S. 1966. Effects of some environmental factors on establishment and development of balsam fir Christmas tree plantations. Vermont Ag. Exp. Sta. Misc. Pub. No. 50.

30) Knight, H. 1963. The effect of nitrogen fertilization on height growth of Douglas-fir on a poor site. For. Chron. 39(4): 403-411.

31) Kozlowski, T. T. 1971. Growth and development of McGraw-Hill, New York. 642 p.

33) Krause, H. H. and W. N. Hamilton. 1981. Foliar analysis for fertilizer recommendations in balsam fir Christmas tree culture. In: Proc. Balsam Fir Update Conf. Univ. of New Brunswick, Forestry Faculty. Fredricton, NB.

34) Krause, H. H. 1988. Mycorrhiza: should it be of concern to Christmas tree growers? In: Balsam Fir Update, Univ. of New Brunswick, Forestry Faculty. Fredricton, NB.

35) Larsen, D. N. 1967. An economic analysis of Christmas tree fertilization. Unpublished thesis, Mich. State Univ.

36) Lavender, D.P. and R. B. Walker. 1979. Nitrogen and related elements in nutrition of forest trees. In: Proc. Forest Fertilization Conf., Univ. of Wash., Instit. of For. Res. Contribution No. 40. pp. 37–47.

37) Marschner, H. 1986. Mineral nutrition of higher plants. Academic Press, New York. 674 p.

38) McClain, K. M. and K. A. Armson. 1976. Effect of water supply, nitrogen and seedbed density on white spruce growth. Soil Sci. Soc. Am. J. Vol. 40: 443-446.

39) Meager, M.D. and K. A. Armson. 1963. The effect of phosphorus placement on the growth of white spruce seedlings. J. of For. 61(12): 918-920.

40) Menge, J. A., et. al. 1977. The effect of fertilization on growth and mycorrhizae numbers in 11 year old loblolly pine plantations. For. Sci. 23(1): 37–44.

41) Miller, R. E. 1979. Response of Douglas-fir to foliar fertilization. In: Proc. Forest Fertilization Conf., Univ. of Wash., Instit. of For. Res. Contribution No. 40. pp. 62–70.

42) Morrison, I. K. 1974. Mineral nutrition of conifers with special reference to nutrient status interpretation: a review of

the literature. Canadian Forestry Service Pub. No. 1343. Ottawa, CN. 74 p.

43) Myers, R. K. 1989. Results after four years of a fertilizer trial in scotch and white pine Christmas production. Purdue Univ. Dept. of For. Bull. No. 195.

44) Otchere-Boateng, J. 1979. Reaction of nitrogen fertilizers in forest soils. In: Proc. Forest Fertilization Conf., Univ. of Wash., Instit. of For. res. Contribution No. 40. pp. 37-47.

45) Powell, G. R. 1981. Understanding the process of shoot development: a background for interpreting the response of balsam fir shoots to pruning and fertilizer. In: Proc. Balsam Fir Update. Univ. of New Brunswick Forestry Faculty. Fredricton, NB.

46) Radwan, M. A. and J. S. Shumway. 1985. Response of Douglas-fir seedlings to nitrogen, sulfur and phosphorus treatments. USDA For. Serv., Pacific NW Exp. Sta. Res. Pap. No. 346.

47) Raid, L. 1985. Effect of fertilizers on foliage development in Scots pine and Norway spruce seedlings. For. Absts. 1986 47(5), entry no. 2071.

48) Schnekenburger, F., et. al. 1985. Effects of nitrogen fertilization and low thinning on snow damage in jack pine. For. Sci. 31(3): 552–556.

49) Shortle, W. C. and K. T. Smith. 1988. Aluminum-induced calcium deficiency in declining red spruce. Science (240): 1017–1018.

50) Stephens, G. R. and R. A. Jaynes. 1975. Effect of soil pH and fertilizer on establishment and growth of Christmas trees. Am. Christmas Tree J., May 1975: 35–37.

51) Sutton, R. F. 1969. Form and development of conifer root systems. Tech. Comm. No. 7, Commonwealth For. Bur., Oxford, England.

52) Tarrant, R. F. and R. R. Silen. 1966. Growth and nutrient uptake of irrigated ponderosa pine after fertilizer treatments. Soil Sci. Soc. Amer. Proc. 30: 796–799.

53) Timmer, V. R., et. al. 1977. Growth response of young balsam fir fertilized with nitrogen, phosphorus, potassium and lime. Can. J. For. Res. 7: 441–446.

54) Timmer, V. R. and E. L. Stone. 1978. Comparative foliar analysis of young balsam fir fertilized with nitrogen, phosphorus, potassium and lime. Soil Sci. Am. J. 42: 125–130.

55) Tisdale, S. L. and W. L. Nelson. 1975. Soil Fertility and Fertilizers, 3rd ed. Macmillan Pub. Co., New York. 694 p.

56) Turner, J. 1979. Interactions of sulfur with nitrogen in forest stands. In: Proc. Forest Fertilization Conf., Univ. of Wash., Instit. of For. Res. Contribution No. 40. pp. 116–125.

57) Turner, D. O. 1966. Color and growth of Douglas-fir Christmas trees as affected by fertilizer application. Soil Sci. Soc. Am. Proc. 30: 792–795.

58) Van den Driessche, R. and J. E. Webber. 1975. Total and soluble nitrogen in Douglas-fir in relation to plant nitrogen status. Can. J. For. Res. Vol 5: 580–585.

59) Van den Driessche, R. 1979. Estimating potential response to fertilizer based on tree tissue and litter analysis. In: Proc. Forest Fertilization Conf., Univ. of Wash., Instit. of For. res. Contribution No. 40. pp. 214–220.

60) ibid. 1984. Nutrient storage retranslocation and relationship of stress to nutrition. In: Nutrition of Plantation Forests, G. D. Brown and E. K. S. Nambiar, editors. Academic Press, New York.

61) ibid. 1988. Response of Douglas-fir to some different fertilizers applied at planting. New Forests 2(2): 89–110.

62) Wheeler, G. L., et. al. 1987. The effects of seedling source, method of weed control and fertilizer on Virginia pine grown for Christmas trees in southern Arkansas. AK Ag. exp. Sta. Bull. No. 898.

63) White, W. C. and D. N. Collins, eds. 1982. The Fertilizer Handbook. The Fertilizer Institute, 1015 18th St., NW, Washington DC, 20036. 274 p.

64) Will, J. B. and J. M. Skelly. 1974. The use of fertilizers to alleviate air pollution damage to white pine (*Pinus strobus*) Christmas trees. Plant Dis. Rep. 58: 150–154.

65) Zimmermann, M. H. and C. L. Brown. 1971. Trees: Structure and Function. Springer-Verlag, New York. 336 p.

APPENDIX D

EQUIPMENT AND MATERIAL SUPPLIERS

Manufacturers and suppliers of micronutrient formulations:

Pure Gro Co.
1276 Halyard Dr.
West Sacramento, CA 95691
916-372-7205

Stoller Chemical Co., Inc.
8582 Katy Freeway
Suite 200
Houston, TX 77024
713-461-2910

Georgia Pacific Corp.
300 W. Laurel St.
Bellingham, WA 98225
206-733-4410

Local fertilizer dealers may also have micronutrient materials that are suitable for Christmas tree use. Other suppliers are listed in The Farm Chemical Handbook (see Appendix C, citation 18, for address)

■■

Manufacturers of plant tissue color charts:

Munsell Color Division
2441 No. Calvert St.
Baltimore, MD 21218
301-243-2171

Royal Horticultural Society
Hilger and Watts, Ltd.
98 St. Pancras Way
London, NW1

■ ■

Equipment suppliers:

Forestry Suppliers, Inc.
P.O. Box 8397
Jackson, MS 39284-8397
1-800-647-5368

Ben Meadows Co.
P.O. Box 80549
Atlanta (Chamblee), GA 30366
1-800-241-6401

Both companies carry soil sampling and testing equipment and supplies, tissue color charts and fertilizer spreaders.

International Reforestation Suppliers, Inc.
P.O. Box 5547
Eugene, OR 97405
1-800-321-1037

Supplier of the backpack system in Figure 13-2.

INDEX

A

Acid rain   41
Aluminum   26, 52
Ammonium   36, 69, 89. *See also* Nitrogen
Ammonium nitrate   36, 69, 89, 94
   handling precautions   72
   to control weeds   88
Ammonium phosphate   75
Ammonium sulfate   72
Available phosphate   51

B

Balsam fir   96, 99
   fertilizer response   99
Boron   43
Branch density   11
Broadcast spreaders   110
bud formation   11
Buffer capacity   26. *See also* Cation exchange capacity

C

Calcium   20, 40, 76
   deficiency symptoms   62
Calcium carbonate equivalent   78
Calcium oxide equivalent   78
Cation exchange capacity   23, 26, 41
   effects of soil texture on   23
Chlorine   43
Chlorosis   41, 61, 94
Conifers
   evolution of   13
Contact exchange   32

Copper   43

D

E

F

M

N

W

Z

This book will inspire you to stretch beyond a positive mindset and experience God's power in a new dimension.

—BOB HARRISON
AMERICA'S INCREASE ACTIVIST

In *Beyond Positive Thinking*, Jim Collins shows us how to focus on God's promises found in the scriptures to realize our unlimited potential and purpose. From revealing how the "Power Twins," Faith and Love, unleash God's purpose in our lives to positive habit formations essential to living a life of joy, *Beyond Positive Thinking* is a compelling book full of insights and encouragement. Jim shows us a practical step-by-step approach implementing tools such as visualization, imagination, and confession of God's Word, which can help us claim our inheritance and see God's plan for our lives become a reality. This is a truly important work for anyone who wants to cultivate a victorious life through Jesus Christ.

—JORDAN RUBIN
NEW YORK TIMES BESTSELLING AUTHOR OF *MAKER'S DIET*
FOUNDER AND CEO, GARDEN OF LIFE

Jim Collins takes the greatest success book ever written, the Bible, and breaks it down into principles that any person can activate in their life. *Beyond Positive Thinking* shows you that while positive thinking and optimism are important and will help you reach great achievement, true success is so much greater and only comes through God's Word. I would encourage anyone interested in reaching their full potential to read this book.

—DR. DAVE MARTIN
AMERICA'S #1 CHRISTIAN SUCCESS COACH

Jim Collins's anointing and skill have come together to give us his absolute best in this book. As a believer and student of Scripture, Jim draws from the richest storehouse of wisdom we have, the Bible; and he does it in a way that is sensible, accurate, and safe. I am now in my sixtieth year of ministry, yet found myself plunging into Jim's Bible truth as if for the first time. This text is excellent for private study as well as for classroom teaching. I recommend it to churches, Sunday schools, small group study, and everywhere that people want motivation to rise from within. This book is not cosmetic and external in motivating the reader. Instead, it contains motivation that is effortless, inspirational, fun, and it will springboard out of you. What more can I say? I was motivated!

—CHARLES CARRIN
CHARLES CARRIN MINISTRIES

I loved reading *Beyond Positive Thinking*. Whether sitting down with Jim or reading his book, I always come away inspired to believe God for bigger things and with a renewed sense of God's purpose in my life. As I read, I found myself underlining whole paragraphs and writing exclamation points in the margins. I would highly recommend *Beyond Positive Thinking* to anyone who is serious about taking life to the next level. Make sure you have your pen ready as you will want to underline and revisit many of Jim's points.

—Dan Plourde
Senior Pastor, Calvary Church, Jupiter, Florida

In *Beyond Positive Thinking*, Jim strategically lays out powerful principles that will help anyone get to a place of unparalleled godly success. Each chapter is rich with insight and easy to understand. For anyone who wants to become better at living out God's best, this is the book to help you in your journey!

—Bishop Fritz Musser
Tabernacle International Church

The truth within this book can change your life and the lives of those around you. I highly recommend it.

—Pastor Bill Earley
The Glory Church

Words like *faith* and *success* have often become clichés in the church's vocabulary, but in this book Jim Collins defines these principles in a tangible and practical way bringing fresh understanding and clear application for implementation and activation into our lives.

—Rick Kendall, President
Victory Ministries and The Body Network

Like all successful pastors, Jim is a great teacher. But I believe that more than anything else, part of his call is to be an encourager. That gift is on display in this book. Many believers become discouraged when their prayers aren't answered in *their* time frame. Jim teaches how to pray and stay in faith until the answer comes. He doesn't just tell you *what* to do, but he tells you *how* to do it. This book will encourage and uplift anyone who reads it.

—Tom Barrett
Southeast Florida District Coordinator,
Gospel Crusade Ministerial Fellowship

Jim Collins has been a voice for positive thinking for many years. *Beyond Positive Thinking* is a current, relevant God-word for today. Jim succinctly articulates the necessity of speaking what God has already said and applying what He has already accomplished. Anyone reading this book and practicing these principles will be more successful and prosperous. In a season of difficulties and limited vision, this book helps you actualize your God-given potential.

—Dr. Norman Benz, Pastor
Covenant Centre International

There are many good motivational and success authors and speakers, but Jim Collins takes you to a different level in his new book, *Beyond Positive Thinking*. He doesn't just tell you how to be successful, he shows you with 100 percent proof.

—Paul Fitzpatrick, Director
PHD Healing Rooms

Beyond Positive Thinking is a must read for every born-again believer, and it will help anybody who is struggling in everyday life. I have been a born-again Christian since 1954, and as I was reading, I learned and relearned the principles of God's Word for my life. *Beyond Positive Thinking* is a book of challenge for change. It was changing me as the words leaped from its pages to my heart.

—Pastor Bob Dailey
Back to Square One Ministries
"From the Heart of the Pastor" TV Internet Program

Beyond Positive Thinking is a fresh revelation of God's Word. As I was reading I found myself saying, "I knew that, but never thought of it that way." This book will impart the principles of Christianity into the hearts of people seeking more success and motivation in their lives.

—Stephen Zoeller
Zoeller Motorsports Ministries

Beyond Positive Thinking will challenge your personal faith as you embark on a journey to a satisfied, joyful life. Jim's grasp of God's Word is unparalleled, and his application of it to our everyday, modern lives is refreshing. Thank you for your inspiring approach on these time-honored scriptures and for reminding us that we must do more than simply hear and read God's Word; we must also speak God's Word. By speaking God's Word, and sharing it with others, it is only then that we become truly aware of its meaning and are able to apply it to our own lives.

—Greg Provenzano
President and Co-Founder, ACN, Inc

This book is needed today more than ever before. As a business owner, this is a great reference book for anyone in business or desiring to start a business. The principles in this book will guarantee anyone's success in life because it is founded on the Word of God.

—Jacinth Waldron, CEO
R.E.I.G.N. Marketing & Consulting LLC

Pastor Jim Collins is a truly inspired and prolific writer. He provides a depth of expression that is both insightful and moving. *Beyond Positive Thinking* is a powerful classic and a must read.

—Dave Gerhardt
Executive Director
Biometics International

Beyond Positive Thinking is a must read for anyone who has a dream, for anyone who desires to achieve, and for anyone who just wants more out of life. Each year dozens of self-help books are released that provide nothing more than recycled platitudes. It is refreshing to see the real source of positive thinking so clearly spelled out in a clear, concise format. Equally refreshing is the acknowledgement that true power does not come from quantum physics or a godless universe, but comes from the love of a merciful God. Jim Collins will teach you how to tap into the force that created the universe. His concepts are scripturally sound and documented. This book will change your life.

—John Whittaker
Lieutenant Colonel, United States Marine Corps, (Ret.)
Nuskin Enterprises Team Elite Distributor and
Million Dollar Circle Earner

Although we are daily bombarded with the advancement of technology, *Beyond Positive Thinking* demands our attention. By reading this book we have to evaluate and then re-evaluate every aspect of our lives, and then instructed by Jim and strengthened by God's Word, our lives can become dynamic and successful.

—Jack Wells
Founder, SchooLife

Jim Collins gives you all you need to know in order to begin to fulfill your God-given destiny and achieve success in the marketplace. Your character, faith, perseverance, and love of God are keys to the life you seek. Jim tells us that character is directly tied to the condition of your heart, and I agree. Have you had a spiritual EKG recently? This book could save your spiritual life and destiny.

—JACK A. SERRA, SR.
1988 ERNST AND YOUNG ENTREPRENEUR OF THE YEAR
FOR NEW JERSEY
AUTHOR OF *REVEALER OF THE ENEMY AND MARKETPLACE* AND
MARRIAGE & SUCCESS: THE SPIRITUAL CONNECTION

I have seen Pastor Jim go from business owner to leader of his own congregation to inspiring professional speaker. He mixes faith and action in everything he does (not to mention, being one of life's true "good guys"). He can show you how to plug into the biblical principles he both preaches and practices in order to achieve massive success in your own life.

—BOB BURG
CO-AUTHOR, *THE GO-GIVER*

Move beyond positive thinking and into a powerful walk of faith. Jim Collins's new book will show you how to embrace all that God has in store for you.

—TOM CRATON, GENERAL MANAGER
WCNO RADIO

Jim Collins has taken the faith message to another level in *Beyond Positive Thinking*. His unique way of linking the love and power of God with faith will transform you from glory to glory. This book will train you to speak, think, and walk in the promises that belong to every believer.

—RICK MADISON
INTERNATIONAL EVANGELIST, AUTHOR, TV HOST

BEYOND
POSITIVE
THINKING

SUCCESS & MOTIVATION
in the SCRIPTURES

JIM COLLINS

EXcel
BOOKS
A STRANG COMPANY

Contents

ACKNOWLEDGMENTS

- First, I want to thank the partners of Beyond Positive Thinking Ministries. Your prayers and support have made this book a reality.

- Many thanks to those who have contributed endorsements. I value your friendship, and I am grateful for your encouragement. We are on a special journey together for the glory of God.

- I would like to give heartfelt thanks to the congregation at Victory in Christ, International. Thank you for your love and faithfulness. I so enjoy sharing the Word of God with you each week.

- My sincere appreciation goes to the team at Excel Books for their willingness to accommodate my special requests, and for the warm reception they extend to my wife Peggy and me every time we visit their offices.

- I want to acknowledge my mom and dad, Ed and Marjorie Collins. My mom is deceased, but I'll always remember her for her unconditional love. Dad, what can I say? You're the best!

- Finally, I thank my heavenly Father for His unending love. I thank my personal Lord and Savior Jesus Christ for calling me into the ministry, and I thank the Holy Spirit for equipping me to preach the Word of God so that lives will be changed.

INTRODUCTION

THE CONCEPT OF positive thinking was put into writing around 1400 B.C. by the author Moses. Later authors through the first century A.D. elaborated on the concept of positive thinking; their works are a collection of sixty-six books collectively known as the Holy Bible. The biblical concept of positive thinking is called "faith."

Positive thinking and faith are similar, but different. Positive thinking attempts to use your own power or an ambiguous higher power to fulfill your own personal agenda. Faith relies on God's power. Positive thinking is all about your agenda and you manipulating your environment. Faith is all about God's agenda and allowing God to fulfill His will and purpose for your life. Positive thinking is all about yourself and what you can get. Faith is all about God and what He can do through you. Positive thinking is filled with pride due to personal manipulation of the spiritual realm. Faith is filled with humility due to the recognition that your power comes from God. Positive thinking is all about the creation; faith is all about the Creator. Positive thinking is about satisfying self; faith is about glorifying God.

The purpose of your life on the earth is to glorify God. Jesus said that He had brought glory to God here on the earth by completing the work that God the Father had given Him to do (John 17:4, AMP). You can also glorify God while you are on the earth by completing the work that God has given you to do. Completing the work that

God has assigned to you includes realizing your God-given dream. Realizing your God-given dream glorifies God!

You were created to have fellowship with God through the process of realizing your God-given dream. Daily fellowship with God begins that process. During your times of fellowship with God, He will give you the details, the plans, and the necessary steps you need to realize your God-given dream. Your God-given dream represents the work that God has given you to do while you are on the earth. Your fellowship with God facilitates the process of realizing your God-given dream.

There are three truths that will enable you to get the most benefit from this book: First, the Bible contains the writings that are inspired by God. (See 2 Timothy 3:16; 2 Peter 1:19–21.) This collection of sixty-six books contains the information that God considered important enough to be preserved through the ages. The efficacy of the Bible as God's Word is based on overwhelming historical, archeological, and prophetic proof.

There is more manuscript support for the Holy Bible, and specifically the New Testament, than for any other body of ancient literature. The Christian's New Testament (books) were the most frequently copied and widely circulated books of antiquity.[1] There are 5,686 Greek and 10,000+ Latin included in 24,970+ total extant (current existing) manuscripts attesting to the integrity of the Holy Bible.[2] Two of the most important manuscripts were written within 300 years after the New Testament was completed, and some virtually complete New Testament books, as well as extensive fragmentary manuscripts of many parts of the New Testament date back to one century from the original writings.[3] In comparison, Homer's Iliad is second (in manuscript support) with only 643 manuscripts that still survive. The first complete preserved text of Homer dates from the thirteenth century.[4] The thirteenth century is 2,100 years after Homer died. No documents of the ancient period are as well attested bibliographically as the New Testament.[5] Nothing is even close.

Second, the Bible is *God's Master Success Book*—His blueprint for your success in life. The principles contained in *God's Master Success*

Book will work for you to the degree that you believe they will work for you. Approach the Bible not as the word of men, but as a divinely inspired message from God to you (1 Thess. 2:13). Accepting God's Word as the source of truth for your life will provide guidance for you. The principles in *God's Master Success Book* will work effectively in your life because the words that God speaks are alive and full of power (Heb. 4:12, AMP). You can be confident that when you act on the principles contained in *God's Master Success Book*, they will become active, operative, energizing, and effective in your life. There is power within the pages of the Bible because those pages contain more than just knowledge and facts; they contain the essence of life itself.

Third, the Bible reveals the will of the Creator of the universe. God's Word was written for you. Look up the scriptures personally and study them for yourself. Always confirm with chapter and verse whenever anyone tells you what the Bible says. Any speaker or writer who is accurately pointing out biblical truths must have taken those truths from the Bible and therefore should know where in the Bible those truths are stated.

As you learn and apply the principles in *God's Master Success Book* you will experience an increased level of motivation and inspiration. Your personal success will be catapulted to a level you have never before known. You will be able to tap into the force that created the universe by understanding who you are, what you have, and what you can do because God made it possible for you to enjoy His life, His nature, and His ability. The power of God makes it possible for you to tap into the force that created the universe.

The answers you need for your success and motivation are already in Scripture. The power that created the universe has always been available to you. This is your time to learn how to tap into the force that created the universe.

Chapter 1

THE POWER TWINS

POSITIVE THINKING IS similar to what God calls "faith." However, positive thinking is limited by the abilities of the individual. Faith has no limits because God has no limits. Faith allows an individual to tap into the force that created the universe.

POSITIVE THINKING AND FAITH

Positive thinking begins and ends with the human mind. Faith is a product of the human spirit. Positive thinking attempts to attain happiness as a result of thinking positive thoughts. Faith provides joy under all circumstances. Positive thinking focuses on thinking positive thoughts. Faith thinks according to the Word of God. Positive thinking hopes to possess the objects of its thoughts. Faith possesses the rights, privileges, and benefits that God has already provided. Positive thinking gives the credit to man. Faith gives the glory to God. Positive thinking strives to win in life based on the ability to maintain a positive attitude. Faith has already secured the victory and responds to the circumstances in life with thanksgiving.

You are an individual miracle of God. You came into this world as pure potentiality. You are the only person with the potential to accomplish a specific task, the realization of your God-given dream.

God created you to do something during your life that only you can do. No other person can fulfill your unique assignment here on the earth. There is no other person to do the work that has been assigned exclusively to you. Realizing your God-given dream requires that you develop your faith. Faith makes it possible for you to receive God's best for your life.

> You were created to have fellowship with God through the process of realizing your God-given dream.

God created you to have fellowship with Him through the process of realizing your God-given dream. Your dreams are God seeking expression through you. God has provided you with everything you need in order to realize your God-given dream. God loves you, God has blessed you, and God has made provision for your success in life.

> "For I know the plans I have for you," declares the LORD, "plans to prosper you and not to harm you, plans to give you hope and a future."
> —JEREMIAH 29:11, NIV

God has a future planned for you. That future includes prosperity, hope, and love. You have been given free will; you can choose to accept the future God has made available to you. You accept the future God has for you through faith. Faith stays focused on the One who is faithful to perform His Word in your life. It is faith that enables you to receive all the provisions that God has already made available for you. Living a life of faith releases God's ability as you realize your God-given dream.

Part of your success in life includes the person you become in the process of realizing your God-given dream. Faith enables you to become everything God says you are, to possess everything God says you have, and to accomplish everything God says you can do.

FAITH RECEIVES GOD'S REWARDS AND BLESSINGS

All things are possible to the person who has faith. Faith accepts God's promises and receives God's rewards and blessings.

> And without faith it is impossible to please God, because anyone who comes to him must believe that he exists and that he rewards those who earnestly seek him.
>
> —HEBREWS 11:6, NIV

God's realm is a faith realm. Believing that God exists and believing that God will reward you both require faith.

> But seek first the kingdom of God and His righteousness, and all these things shall be added to you.
>
> —MATTHEW 6:33

Jesus stated that when you put God and His kingdom first in your life, you will receive the things you need in your life. Jesus stated that when you live right the door to God's provision is opened to you. You seek both God and His kingdom by diligently studying the principles in *God's Master Success Book*. Seeking God includes spending time with Him. Whenever you spend time learning God's Word you are spending time with God. Seeking God includes learning God's Word by hearing God's Word.

> So then faith comes by hearing, and hearing by the word of God.
>
> —ROMANS 10:17

Faith in God is faith in His Word. Your faith will grow as you diligently study God's Word. Your confidence in God's success principles will increase in direct proportion to your knowledge and understanding of those principles. Your knowledge and understanding will increase as you hear God's Word. The results you obtain from the study of God's Word will be in direct proportion to your application of God's success principles in your daily life.

It is faith in action that receives the rewards and blessings of God. The success principles in God's Word will work for anyone who acts on them. Action is the catalyst that releases the power of God.

The Power Twins—Faith and Love

Faith is the first half of the Power Twins.

> Now faith is being sure of what we hope for and
> certain of what we do not see.
> —Hebrews 11:1, niv

Faith is being sure of what you hope for. Hope is confident expectation that you will realize your God-given dream. Your faith is an essential element in the realization of your God-given dream. Faith sees your dream as a reality before your eyes see the end result. Faith releases the ability of God and causes events and circumstances to unfold according to the image of your dream. Faith does not wait for the five physical senses to confirm your dream because faith knows that God's promises are trustworthy. Faith is knowing that you will realize your God-given dream.

Love is the second half of the Power Twins.

> For [if we are] in Christ Jesus, neither circumcision
> nor uncircumcision counts for anything, but only
> faith activated and energized and expressed and
> working through love.[1]
> —Galatians 5:6, amp

Love activates your faith.[2] Love is what empowers your faith to receive the rewards and blessings of God. Love is what energizes your faith to realize your God-given dream.

The phrase "love your neighbor as yourself" is repeated eight times in the Bible. (See Leviticus 19:18; Matthew 19:19; 22:39; Mark 12:31; Luke 10:27; Romans 13:9; Galatians 5:14; James 2:8.) The first person you need to love is yourself. You must have love for yourself in order to effectively share your love with others. A healthy self-image and a high level of self-esteem enable and empower you to give love to others. God is love and Jesus commanded His followers to love one another with the God-kind of love.

> This is My commandment, that you love one another as I have loved you.
>
> —John 15:12

Jesus' quote, "as I have loved you," refers to the God-kind of love. Jesus expressed the character of God, and He also exhibited the characteristics of the God-kind of love.

The Greek word for the love that Jesus spoke of is *agape*, which refers to the God-kind of love.[3]

> Action is the catalyst that releases the power of God.

The characteristics of the God-kind of love, agape love, are found in 1 Corinthians chapter 13:

> Love suffers long and is kind; love does not envy; love does not parade itself, is not puffed up; does not behave rudely, does not seek its own, is not provoked, thinks no evil; does not rejoice in iniquity, but rejoices in truth; bears all things, believes all things, hopes all things, endures all things. Love never fails.
>
> —1 Corinthians 13:4–8

The characteristics of agape love culminate with the victory cry "Love never fails." God is love and God never fails. As you live a life of faith and express that faith by walking in love, you never fail.

Love never fails; love always succeeds. When you walk in love, you always succeed!

The Power Twins at Work

Love, agape love, is what makes faith effective. Faith grows as you practice walking in love.

> And if I had such faith that I could move moun-
> tains, but didn't love others, I would be nothing.
> —1 Corinthians 13:2, nlt

Were you to possess the faith that could remove the problems, challenges, and obstacles from your life, but were lacking in love, you would have accomplished nothing in the eyes of God. You must practice the God-kind of love to fully develop your faith. Unless you walk in love, your faith will always be shallow and ineffective.

> When you walk in love, you always succeed!

> So Jesus answered and said to them, "Have faith
> in God. For assuredly, I say to you, whoever says
> to this mountain, 'Be removed and be cast into the
> sea,' and does not doubt in his heart, but believes
> that those things he says will be done, he will have
> whatever he says. Therefore I say to you, what-
> ever things you ask when you pray, believe that
> you receive them, and you will have them. And
> whenever you stand praying, if you have anything
> against anyone, forgive him, that your Father in
> heaven may also forgive you your trespasses."
> —Mark 11:22–25

Jesus begins in Mark 11:22 by saying you must have faith in God. He then says to release your faith with your words. The grand finale of faith takes place by believing that you have received the things you asked for when you prayed. Next, you are cautioned to search your heart to see if you are harboring any unforgiveness or ill will toward any other person. One of the highest forms of love is to forgive someone. You are admonished to forgive the offenses of others so that you will receive forgiveness for your own trespasses. Love, in the form of forgiveness, makes your faith even more effective. The faith that pleases God says what it wants, believes that it has it, and forgives others.

> We are bound to thank God always for you, brethren, as it is fitting, because your faith grows exceedingly, and the love of every one of you all abounds toward each other.
> —2 Thessalonians 1:3

Intimate fellowship with God becomes available to you as you grow in faith and love. The Power Twins, Faith and Love, will lead you into fellowship; not just fellowship with other people but fellowship with God. Intimate fellowship with God is available to you in each of the following areas:

With His Life (John 10:10)

With His Nature (2 Pet. 1:4)

With His Ability (Phil. 4:13)

With His Victory (Rom. 8:37)

With His Love (Col. 1:13)

With His Health (1 Pet. 2:24)

With His Authority (Luke 10:19)

With His Righteousness (2 Cor. 5:21)

With His Success (3 John 2)

With His Riches (Phil. 4:19)

Your intimacy with God grows deeper as your faith and love grow. The Power Twins, Faith and Love, will lead the way for your life-changing experience.

> And we also [especially] thank God continually for this, that when you received the message of God [which you heard] from us, you welcomed it not as the word of [mere] men, but as what it truly is,

> the Word of God, which is effectually at work in
> you who believe [exercising its superhuman power
> in those who adhere to and trust in and rely on it].
>
> —1 THESSALONIANS 2:13, AMP

God's Word will work its superhuman power in you and produce results in your life that are far over and above all that you dare ask or think, infinitely beyond your highest prayers, desires, thoughts, hopes, or dreams (Eph. 3:20, AMP). When you take action on the principles contained in *God's Master Success Book* your faith and love will experience tremendous growth. The Power Twins will release the ability of God, and God's ability will assist you in achieving your goals and realizing your God-given dream. The Power Twins, Faith and Love, make God's power effective in your life.

> Faith and Love make God's power effective in your life.

As you learn how to tap into the force that created the universe, the same power that created the heavens and the earth will be available to help you realize your God-given dream. Your life will never be the same again!

1. You were created to have fellowship with God through the process of realizing your God-given dream.

2. God has a future planned for you that includes prosperity, hope, and love.

3. God created you to do something during your life that only you can do. There is no other person to do the work that has been assigned exclusively to you.

4. Your dreams are God seeking expression through you.

5. God has provided you with everything you need in order to realize your God-given dream.

6. Part of your success includes the person you become in the process of realizing your God-given dream.

7. Faith enables you to become everything God says you are, to possess everything God says you have, and to accomplish everything God says you can do.

8. Faith in God is faith in His Word.

9. Faith accepts God's promises and receives God's rewards and blessings.

10. Action is the catalyst that releases the power of God.

11. Love, agape love, is what makes faith effective.

12. Your faith grows as you practice walking in love.

13. One of the highest forms of love is in forgiving someone.

14. The faith that pleases God says what it wants, believes that it has it, and forgives others.

15. Faith working through love allows you to tap into the force that created the universe.

16. The Power Twins, Faith and Love, make God's power effective in your life.

Chapter 2

You and the Force That Created the Universe

God has designed a foundation for you to build your life upon. Building on this foundation will allow you to realize your God-given dream. This foundation will help you reach your full potential and ensure lasting success. The following scripture lays the foundation that will enable you to tap into the force that created the universe:

> Therefore, if anyone is in Christ, he is a new creation; old things have passed away; behold, all things have become new.
>
> —2 Corinthians 5:17

A new creation has the ability to tap into the force that created the universe. The answers to the following four questions will help you understand the significance of being a new creation:

1. What does it mean to be "in Christ"?
2. What does it mean to be a new creation?
3. What are the old things that have passed away?
4. What things have become new?

1. What does it mean to be "in Christ"?

The phrase "in Christ" refers to a relationship between God and an individual. It is not because you belong to a particular church or attend a particular religious meeting that you have the benefits of God; it is because you belong to Jesus. To be in Christ is to be a child of God, a son or daughter of the Creator of the universe.

> For you are all children of God through faith in Christ Jesus.
> —GALATIANS 3:26, NLT

You are in the family of God through faith in Jesus Christ. God is your spiritual Father, and it was He who created the universe. God created everything, and you, as a child of God, have become an heir to it all. God created mankind to have fellowship with Him, to have dominion over all the earth, and to enjoy life in union and communion with Him. Fellowship includes intimate conversation and communion. One of the greatest desires of an earthly parent is to have fellowship, intimate conversation, and communion with his children, and so it is with your heavenly Father. You can talk to God just as you would talk to a loving parent.

> To be in Christ is to be a son or daughter of the Creator of the universe.

> And because you are sons, God has sent forth the Spirit of His Son into your hearts, crying out, "Abba, Father!"
> —GALATIANS 4:6

The phrase "Abba, Father"[1] refers to a close, intimate relationship with God. "Abba, Father!" is expressive of an especially close relationship between a child and a loving father. God the Father is a God of love, and you are an heir of God through Christ.

> Therefore, you are no longer a slave (bond servant)
> but a son; and if a son, then [it follows that you
> are] an heir by the aid of God, through Christ.
> —GALATIANS 4:7, AMP

You have been given an inheritance to enjoy. As a son or daughter of God, your inheritance is revealed to you in Christ. (See Ephesians 1:11.) You have become an heir to everything God says you are, everything God says you have, and everything God says you can do. As a child of God, you have access to all God's resources. As God's heir, you can claim what He has provided for you.

You are God's child; you have been adopted into His royal family (Eph. 1:5, NLT). Your inheritance includes all the blessings of God. You have the ability to receive the provision God has already provided for you. You can live an enjoyable and satisfying life. God's will for your life is that you embrace the rights, privileges, and responsibilities of a child in God's family.

> For we are God's [own] handiwork (His workman-
> ship), recreated in Christ Jesus, [born anew] that
> we may do those good works which God predes-
> tined (planned beforehand) for us [taking paths
> which He prepared ahead of time], that we should
> walk in them [living the good life which He prear-
> ranged and made ready for us to live].
> —EPHESIANS 2:10, AMP

The Greek word translated *workmanship* is the word *poiema*, from which we get the English word poem. It literally means "a work of art." God created you, His work of art, with the potential to accomplish the work He gave you to do. Your work, the path you are to take, is the realization of your God-given dream. God made provision for you to be able to realize your God-given dream, and that provision was made before you were placed on this earth. You

17

receive the blessings of God into your life as you fulfill the plan He has for you on this earth.

You are a loved and cherished one-of-a-kind creation. You are special, unique, and irreplaceable. God has specific plans for you that nobody else can accomplish. Only you can complete the work that has been assigned to you. Only you can realize your God-given dream.

You were created not just to exist, but to live a fulfilled and significant life. God prearranged and made available everything that is necessary for you to live the good life. The "good works" God planned ahead of time for you to accomplish include the realization of your God-given dream.

> You are a loved and cherished one-of-a-kind creation.

2. What does it mean to be a new creation?

To understand the new creation, you must first understand the new birth, because out of the new birth comes the new creation. Your interpretation of the new birth will determine your perspective on your entire Christian experience.

> There was a man named Nicodemus, a Jewish religious leader who was a Pharisee. After dark one evening, he came to speak with Jesus. "Rabbi," he said, "we all know that God has sent you to teach us. Your miraculous signs are evidence that God is with you." Jesus replied, "I tell you the truth, unless you are born again, you cannot see the Kingdom of God." "What do you mean?" exclaimed Nicodemus. "How can an old man go back into his mother's womb and be born again?" Jesus replied, "I assure you, no one can enter the Kingdom of God without being born of water and the Spirit. Humans can reproduce only human life, but the Holy Spirit gives birth

to spiritual life. So don't be surprised when I say,
'You must be born again.'"

—JOHN 3:1–7, NLT

Jesus told Nicodemus that he must be born again to be able to
see and enter the kingdom of God. Nicodemus was confused about
how a grown man could be born a second time. Jesus ended Nicodemus' confusion by explaining that he did not need to be born
physically a second time, he needed to be born again spiritually.

The new birth takes place in
the human spirit. It is the human
spirit, the part of man that communicates with God, which needs
to be reconnected to the source of
all life. It is not the physical part

> The new birth is
> the re-creation of the
> human spirit.

of a person that needs to be born again, but the spiritual part of a
person. To be born again is to become a new creation. The new birth
is the re-creation of the human spirit.

> That whoever believes in Him should not perish
> but have eternal life. For God so loved the world
> that He gave His only begotten Son, that whoever
> believes in Him should not perish but have ever-
> lasting life.
>
> —JOHN 3:15–16

> I assure you, most solemnly I tell you, he who
> believes in Me [who adheres to, trusts in, relies on,
> and has faith in Me] has (now possesses) eternal
> life.
>
> —JOHN 6:47, AMP

Eternal life (also translated as everlasting life) is the life and nature of God, which is imparted to a person's spirit at the new birth
making them a new creation. It is the life and nature of God that

19

makes a person a new creation. This new creation has spiritual union with Deity.

> Eternal life is the life and nature of God.

Eternal life does not begin after physical death. Eternal life is a present possession, not something that is obtained at a future date. Eternal life begins at the new birth and continues for eternity. Eternal life starts here on the earth the moment a person becomes a new creation.

A born-again Christian is one who has received eternal life; one who has received the life and nature of God. Receiving eternal life is a supernatural experience that occurs during the rebirth of every child of God.

3. What are the old things that have passed away?

The biblical story of the creation of mankind includes the account of the fall of mankind. The old things are a direct result of the fall of mankind. The story of the creation of mankind and the account of the fall of the human race are found in the first book of the Bible, Genesis.

> Then God said, "Let Us make man in Our image, according to Our likeness; let them have dominion over the fish of the sea, over the birds of the air, and over the cattle, over all the earth and over every creeping thing that creeps on the earth." So God created man in His own image; in the image of God He created him; male and female He created them.
>
> —Genesis 1:26–27

God created mankind to be a reflection of His own image, a reflection of His own nature. God created human beings to be like Him and to be the agents of His authority on the earth.

> Then the Lord God formed man from the dust of the ground and breathed into his nostrils the breath or spirit of life, and man became a living being.
>
> —GENESIS 2:7, AMP

It is at this point in the story of the creation of mankind that God created man physically. God had already created man in His own image and likeness, a spiritual being. God then put the spirit (man) He had created into a physical body.

God then put the man, the spirit with a physical body, into the Garden of Eden and gave him a specific command.

> The LORD God put the man in the garden of Eden to care for it and work it. The LORD God commanded him, "You may eat the fruit from any tree in the garden, but you must not eat the fruit from the tree which gives the knowledge of good and evil. If you ever eat fruit from that tree, you will die!"
>
> —GENESIS 2:15–17, NCV

God's specific command was to refrain from eating the fruit from the tree of the knowledge of good and evil. God warned that disobedience would result in death. This type of death would cause the fall of mankind and the fall of mankind would bring the onset of the old things.

The next event recorded in the creation story of mankind led to the dilemma the human race finds itself in today.

> The serpent was the shrewdest of all the wild animals the LORD God had made. One day he asked the woman, "Did God really say you must not eat the fruit from any of the trees in the garden?" "Of course we may eat fruit from

> the trees in the garden," the woman replied. "It's
> only the fruit from the tree in the middle of
> the garden that we are not allowed to eat. God
> said, 'You must not eat it or even touch it; if you
> do, you will die.'" "You won't die!" the serpent
> replied to the woman. "God knows that your
> eyes will be opened as soon as you eat it, and you
> will be like God, knowing both good and evil."
> The woman was convinced. She saw that the tree
> was beautiful and its fruit looked delicious, and
> she wanted the wisdom it would give her. So she
> took some of the fruit and ate it. Then she gave
> some to her husband, who was with her, and he
> ate it, too.
>
> —Genesis 3:1–6, nlt

God had made a woman to be a helper and companion for the
man. The actions taken by the man and the woman resulted in disobedience.[2] Both the man and the woman knew that disobedience
would result in death. However, the consequence of their disobedience, death, did not happen immediately.

> At that moment their eyes were opened, and they
> suddenly felt shame at their nakedness. So they
> sewed fig leaves together to cover themselves.
> When the cool evening breezes were blowing, the
> man and his wife heard the Lord God walking
> about in the garden. So they hid from the Lord
> God among the trees. Then the Lord God called
> to the man, "Where are you?" He replied, "I heard
> you walking in the garden, so I hid. I was afraid
> because I was naked." "Who told you that you
> were naked?" the Lord God asked. "Have you
> eaten from the tree whose fruit I commanded you
> not to eat?" The man replied, "It was the woman

you gave me who gave me the fruit, and I ate it."
Then the LORD God asked the woman, "What
have you done?" "The serpent deceived me," she
replied. "That's why I ate it."

—GENESIS 3:7–13, NLT

The type of death Adam and Eve experienced was not physical
death, but spiritual death. God had warned that death would be
the result of disobedience. Spiritual death was the immediate consequence of violating God's command. Physical death was the
delayed consequence of spiritual death. Just as God created mankind twice, first spiritually and then physically, there are two kinds
of death, spiritual death and physical death.

Spiritual death occurred when Adam and Eve disobeyed God.
Spiritual death resulted in broken fellowship with God. Adam and
Eve had always known the privilege of regular conversation with
God. Their intimate fellowship
with God was now ended. The
loss of that privilege was extended
to the future generations of the
human race. All future genera-
tions of humanity became subject to the same spiritual death that
Adam and Eve experienced.

> Spiritual death is separation
> from God.

Spiritual death caused separation from God. When God created
Adam, Adam possessed spiritual life, the life and nature of God.
Due to Adam's disobedience (sin) all of humanity became as he had
become, separated from God and spiritually dead.

> When Adam sinned, sin entered the world.
> Adam's sin brought death, so death spread to
> everyone, for everyone sinned....Still, everyone
> died—from the time of Adam to the time of
> Moses—even those who did not disobey an
> explicit commandment of God, as Adam did.

> Now Adam is a symbol, a representation of
> Christ, who was yet to come.
> —Romans 5:12, 14, nlt

The human race is separated from God and spiritually dead because of Adam's sin. Sin caused spiritual death, and spiritual death separated the human race from God. The old things that have passed away are spiritual death and being separated from God.

4. What things have become new?

Spiritual death and being separated from God have passed away. God, the Creator of the universe, has once again become the spiritual Father of those who choose to be spiritually reborn (born again). When a person is reunited with God, he or she receives eternal life (spiritual life).

> For just as [because of their union of nature] in
> Adam all people die, so also [by virtue of their
> union of nature] shall all in Christ be made alive.
> —1 Corinthians 15:22, amp

Every person who is in Christ is spiritually alive. The things that have become new include a re-created spirit filled with eternal life and an inheritance as an heir of God. The inheritance of a child of God includes immediate entitlement to the blessings of God. The blessings of God include the promises of God.

> For as many as are the promises of God, they all
> find their Yes [answer] in Him [Christ].
> —2 Corinthians 1:20, amp

The promises of God make the benefits of God available to the child of God. The benefits of God are threefold. First, who you are in Christ; second, what you have in Christ; and third, what you can do because you are in Christ. Your inheritance—who you are, what you have, and what you can do—is found within the "in Him" scriptures. There are more than one hundred "in Him" scriptures in the New Testament. The "in Him" scriptures contain the following, or similar, phrases:

> In Christ, in Christ Jesus, in Him, in Himself, in the Beloved, in the Lord, in Whom, in His Son, by Christ, by Him, by Himself, by His Blood, by His Grace, from Whom, of Christ, of Him, of His Love, through Christ, through Him, with Christ, with Him, in Me, in My Love, in My Name, in His Name.

The rights and privileges of your inheritance are also found within the "in Him" scriptures. Most of the "in Him" scriptures are found in the Gospel of John and in the Epistles.[3] The Epistles are found in the New Testament from the book of Romans through the book of Jude. The Epistles are letters that were written to established churches or for the church as a whole.[4] The Christians of today are the modern day church. The Epistles are timeless, they were written for the benefit of all Christians throughout all time. The principles expressed in the Epistles are as relevant today as they were two thousand years ago.

The things that have become new include who you are; you are a child of God. The things that have become new include what you have; you have eternal life and an inheritance from God. The things that have become new include what you can do; you can realize your God-given dream.

Enjoying these new things starts with your relationship with God. When you choose to

> Your inheritance is found within the "in Him" scriptures.

receive eternal life, your human spirit is re-created and filled with God's life and nature. The life and nature of God give you access to God's ability. You can have that same ability within you in the person of the Holy Spirit. You receive the Spirit of God when you are born again and filled with the Holy Spirit. You can be born again and filled with the Holy Spirit today![5]

CHAPTER PRINCIPLES

1. God planned a foundation upon which you can realize your God-given dream.

2. A new creation has the ability to tap into the force that created the universe.

3. To be in Christ is to be a child of God, a son or daughter of the Creator of the universe.

4. As a child of God, you have access to all God's resources. As God's heir, you can claim what He has provided for you.

5. God's will for your life is that you embrace the rights, privileges, and responsibilities of a child in God's family.

6. Your work, the path you are to take, is the realization of your God-given dream.

7. God has specific plans for you that nobody else can accomplish.

8. It is the human spirit, the part of man that communicates with God, which needs to be reconnected to the source of all life.

9. The new birth is the re-creation of the human spirit.

10. Eternal life, the life and nature of God, is a present possession.

11. There are two kinds of death, spiritual death and physical death.

12. Your inheritance—who you are, what you have, and what you can do—is found within the "in Him" scriptures.

13. The benefits of God are threefold. First, who you are in Christ—you are a child of God. Second, what you have in Christ—you have eternal life and an inheritance. Third, what you can do in Christ—you can realize your God-given dream!

Chapter 3

RECEIVING YOUR
HEART'S DESIRE

PART OF REALIZING your God-given dream is receiving your heart's desire.[1] You will be able to receive the desires of your heart to the degree that you delight yourself in Him. To delight yourself in Him requires that you make a decision to live according to who you are in Christ.

> Delight yourself also in the LORD, And He shall
> give you the desires of your heart.
>
> —PSALM 37:4

To delight yourself in the Lord is to be in Christ and to enjoy that reality. To delight yourself in the Lord requires that you make a decision to live according to God's will for your life. God's will is that the reality of who you are in Christ becomes the dominant desire of your heart.

> May He grant your heart's desires and make all
> your plans succeed.
>
> —PSALM 20:4, NLT

It is encouraging to know that it is God's will to give you your heart's desire. It is encouraging to know that it is God's will to make all your plans succeed. When you make a decision to live according to who you are in Christ, God will cause your thoughts to become agreeable to His will. Your plans will succeed, you will receive your heart's desire, and you will realize your God-given dream.

> Your heart's desire includes what you have a passion to be, to do, and to have.

Your heart's desire includes what you have a passion to be, to do, and to have. Your heart's desire includes the improvements you want to make in your life. Your heart's desire may include a closer relationship with your family or a stronger marriage. Perhaps your heart's desire includes improving your health. You may desire more prosperity in your business or career. You may desire to give more money to your church or your favorite charity. Perhaps identifying your God-given dream and implementing God's plan for your life would be your heart's desire.

Visualize Your Ideal Day

If you had no limitations on your income or your life, what would your ideal day be like? Create an image of your ideal day in your mind. What time would your day start? Imagine the start of your ideal day with waking up at your personal ideal time.

How will you start your day? Perhaps the first thing you do is thank God for all the blessings He has given you. One of those blessings might be the ability to start your day when you want because God has blessed you with a flexible schedule. Will you spend some quiet time in fellowship with God reading His Word? The Bible is not only the "Owner's Manual" for your life, it is also the "Success Manual" for your life!

Will the rest of your morning include some kind of exercise? Perhaps some light stretching and a walk or a bike ride. You may prefer working out at your favorite health club. Your body was created to be active, and it feels good to exercise once you start to get in shape.

Your ideal day may start with a nice refreshing shower and then a nutritious breakfast. Your breakfast may include enjoying some fresh fruit, some oatmeal, or perhaps some eggs with a fresh baked bagel.

Will you be doing some form of work today, or is today going to be a relaxing day off? What kind of work will you be doing, and who will you be working with? Will you be working from your home office or at a location outside your home? Perhaps your day will be filled with the work of ministry. In the Bible, the words *ministry* and *service* are synonymous. If you are a Christian you are a minister, and when you are serving you are ministering. Serving those less fortunate than yourself will send your self-esteem soaring and give you the deep inner satisfaction that comes with knowing that you are really making a difference.

Do you have a busy evening planned with your family, or will it be a quiet evening alone with that special person in your life? Will you eat dinner out or enjoy a home cooked meal together? Perhaps tonight is a special night for you and your spouse because you are celebrating the financial freedom that you achieved together.

There are three good reasons for creating and visualizing your ideal day. First, to reinforce that your dreams are God seeking expression through you. Second, to know that God wants to grant your heart's desire and make all your plans succeed. Third, creating your ideal day is a vital discovery because a successful life is a series of successful days.

Your daily habits are creating your future. You must discover where you want to go before you can develop the habits that will take you there. Use some of your quiet time to allow yourself to visualize your ideal day. Slip away occasionally on a mind relaxation journey by imagining where you want your habits to take you.

> A successful life is a series of successful days. Your daily habits are creating your future.

Create the Kind of Life You Want

You can create the kind of life you really want. Many people have a difficult time deciding what kind of life they want to live, and because they never figure out what they want from life, they leave this life with their music still inside of them.

A better approach to finding out what you want from life is to start the process by finding out what God's will is for you during your life. The general answer to this personal dilemma is found in *God's Master Success Book*. God's general will for your life is contained within the principles outlined in His Word. The specific answer to this personal dilemma is found by identifying the unique talents, gifts, skills, and abilities that will allow you to receive your heart's desire and realize your God-given dream.

God gave you talents, gifts, skills, and abilities that will allow you to receive your heart's desire and realize your God-given dream. You have unique talents, gifts, skills, and abilities that nobody else possesses. It is your responsibility to identify those talents, gifts, skills, and abilities and then focus on becoming excellent at them. When you become excellent at them, you will be using them for God's glory. As you develop your potential, you will discover what God specifically intends for you to do with your life.

At first, being so concerned with what you want may appear to be a little self-centered. However, discovering what you want is not leaving God out and it is not being concerned with only yourself. Discovering what you really want is not about being selfish; it is about taking responsibility for the life that God has prepared for you to live. If the kind of life you want is in agreement with God's will, then it will bring glory to God. The ultimate goal of your existence is to glorify God by doing what He has called you to do, which is realizing your God-given dream!

Living the kind of life you want is very different from pursuing wants solely by acquiring material things. Many people are living lives void of love, joy, peace, and contentment. It is important to realize that these qualities cannot be obtained through the pursuit and accumulation of things, but they can be obtained by living a life according to God's will.

The best way to predict your future is to create it! Creating your future starts with knowing what kind of life you want, knowing what your future is supposed to look like, and knowing what you must become in order to receive everything you want. The following seven questions will help you identify what it is you want to be, to do, and to have:

1. What kind of life do you want?
2. What have you always dreamed of doing, but were afraid to attempt?
3. What kind of work would you do if you did not need the money?
4. What are your unique talents, gifts, skills, and abilities?
5. What has God called you to do?
6. What does your ideal day look like?
7. What one great thing would you do if you knew you could not fail?

Writing the answers to those questions is proof that you can live your dreams. You just need to identify what kind of life you want. If you can see it with your imagination, you can experience it in your life. Your answers to those questions will help you identify what you love to do and encourage your passion for the desires that God has placed within you.

The rich and satisfying life you are destined to live starts with what you want to do with your life. God gave you His life, His nature, and His ability so that you could tap into the force that created the universe. You can harness that power as an aid to help you live your dreams. God created you to have fellowship with Him so that the two of you could work together as you fulfill your God-given potential on this earth. God created you to have fellowship with Him through the process of realizing your God-given dream. God has already provided you with an abundance of life; now it is up to you to create your own abundant life here on earth.

> I came that they may have and enjoy life, and have
> it in abundance (to the full, till it overflows).
> —John 10:10, amp

The word *life* that Jesus is speaking of refers to the God-kind of life. The Greek word that is translated as *life* is *zoe*. The word *zoe* refers to life as God has it.[2] Jesus came to give you an abundance of God's life. He gave you abundant life from heaven so you could create your own abundant life here on earth. Jesus came to the earth so you could have *and* enjoy life, and have it in abundance!

Most people desire to have abundant life, and Jesus said that He came to make abundant life available. You will personally experience the reality of abundant life as you learn how to tap into the force that created the universe.

_____

The best way to predict your
future is to create it!

_____

The formula that will enable you to receive your heart's desire and realize your God-given dream is contained in *God's Master Success Book*. Everything you need for the rest of your life has already been provided for you in Christ. It is your responsibility to receive that entire provision into your life. That provision begins with your salvation.

Your salvation was made available through the sacrifice of Jesus Christ more than two thousand years ago. However, you did not receive your salvation until you acted according to God's Word. You received the provision of salvation only after you took action. All of God's promises are available to you, and all of those promises can be received by acting according to God's Word. Two of those promises include prosperity and health (3 John 1:2). To receive any of God's promises, including prosperity and health, you must put God's Word into practice in your life. The Word of God will work for anyone who acts according to the instructions contained in *God's Master Success Book.*

> If you confess with your mouth that Jesus is Lord and believe in your heart that God raised him from the dead, you will be saved.
>
> —ROMANS 10:9, NLT

You received your salvation by confessing that Jesus is your Lord and believing in your heart that God raised Him from the dead. You received your salvation by confessing and believing, and now the rest of your Christian life is to be based on that truth. You will continue to receive everything that God has promised you by confessing and believing. When you acted on God's Word, by confessing and believing, God supernaturally removed your old sinful nature of spiritual death. Spiritual death prevented you from having and enjoying abundant life. God replaced the old nature of spiritual death with a new nature filled with spiritual life (God's life, which is eternal life). Now God's ability is available so that you can enjoy an abundant life.

When you received eternal life, the same power that spoke the earth and the sun into existence came to make its home in you. The same power that raised Christ from the dead came to live on the inside of you in your re-created spirit. The same power that created the heavens and the earth became available to you. Your spirit is alive with the force that created the universe and that power is waiting for you to take action by believing and speaking. (See 2 Corinthians 4:13.)

> For assuredly, I say to you, whoever says to this mountain, "Be removed and be cast into the sea," and does not doubt in his heart, but believes that those things he says will come to pass, he will have whatever he says.
>
> —MARK 11:23

Creating the kind of life you want starts by speaking words out of a believing heart. You are going to have whatever you believe in your heart and say with your mouth. This is the key to manifesting the promises of God and enjoying your provision in Christ. "Jesus Christ is the same yesterday, today, and forever" (Heb. 13:8). Believing and speaking will work just as wonderfully today as it did when Jesus told His disciples, "whoever says...and does not doubt in his heart, but believes that those things he says will come to pass, he will have whatever he says." Believing and speaking is how you receive all of God's promises. Whatever the heart believes, the mouth confesses.

> For with the heart one believes unto righteousness, and with the mouth confession is made unto salvation.
> —ROMANS 10:10

When you acted according to God's Word you changed your eternal destiny. You changed the location of where you are going to spend your eternal future. You are going to live in the presence of God forever. This change took place by believing and speaking. You can also change your future here on the earth by believing and speaking. The way you change your life today and tomorrow is with words spoken out of a believing heart. You can live "a rich and satisfying life"! (John 10:10, NLT).

> Jesus addressed the issue of what you will have in your life; you will have what you believe in your heart and say with your mouth.

You can speak your future into existence the same way you spoke your salvation into existence. When you learn how to put your words to work in your life by creating the life you want, then according to Jesus, that is what you will have. Jesus addressed the issue of what you will have in your life; you will have what you believe in your heart and say with your mouth.

If you believe in who you are in Christ, you can do anything! Believing is acting according to God's Word. *To believe* means "to live in accordance with." The principles in *God's Master Success Book* work in your life as you live in accordance with them. *Believing* is an action verb. What you do is the real proof of the kind of life you really want to live. After all the excuses, the proof of how motivated you are is revealed by what you do.

THE ATTITUDE OF FAITH

The secret to receiving all the benefits of your salvation is to adopt an attitude of faith. Faith is the receptive power of your re-created spirit that takes what God offers you in His Word. The proof that you will receive your heart's desire and realize your God-given dream is based on the integrity of God's Word. Faith declares that God's Word is true in your life today.

> Now faith is the substance of things hoped for, the evidence of things not seen.
> —HEBREWS 11:1

Faith is the substance that makes what you see out of what you do not see. Faith gives substance to your heart's desire. The only evidence you need is the picture you hold in your mind of you being in possession of your heart's desire. The thought-image of your heart's desire is the substance of things hoped for and the evidence of things not seen. Faith provides the assurance that your mental image will become a reality. Faith is the proof that your mental images will manifest in the physical realm.

> God, who gives life to the dead and calls those things which do not exist as though they did.
> —ROMANS 4:17

God speaks of nonexistent things as if they already existed. You are to follow God's example to create the kind of life you want.

Creating your future starts with your words. You can speak your future into existence. It is up to you whether or not you follow God's example. It is up to you whether or not you receive your heart's desire and realize your God-given dream. Your words are the proof of how certain you are of what you do not see. What you confess with your mouth and believe in your heart is what will come to pass in your life. Jesus said, "The mouth speaks the things that are in the heart" (Matt. 12:34, NCV). Your words are the proof of what you really believe. If you go around saying, "I don't feel good," "I'm sick," "I can't do it," "I don't have enough money to pay my bills," etc., you are going to have what Jesus said you are going to have; whatever you say.

> Now faith is the assurance (the confirmation, the title deed) of the things [we] hope for, being the proof of things [we] do not see and the conviction of their reality [faith perceiving as real fact what is not revealed to the senses].
> —Hebrews 11:1, AMP

Faith believes it has something before the five senses give confirmation. Just because something is not revealed to the five physical senses does not mean it does not exist. God is always doing something in your life that you cannot see. Faith makes invisible things real. Faith is the proof that what you cannot see will eventually become a reality in your life.

> For we walk by faith, not by sight.
> —2 Corinthians 5:7

The phrase *not by sight* means you should not conduct yourself solely according to the sense realm. You are to be governed by faith and not solely by what you see or feel. If God had waited until He could see the sun before He said, "Let there be light" (Gen. 1:3), nothing would have happened. The same is true in your life. You can change your life starting with your words. Change takes place by faith. Change takes place as you call those things that do not exist as though they did.

God used the principle of speaking things into existence to create the material universe. You were created in the image of God, and you can follow God's example by using the same principle to create the kind of life you want.

> By faith we understand that the worlds were framed
> by the word of God, so that the things which are
> seen were not made of things which are visible.
> —HEBREWS 11:3

There are two sources of information: the physical realm that can be seen and the spiritual realm which cannot be seen. The things which are visible refer to the physical realm; the things that are not seen refer to the spiritual realm. The physical realm was *not* made out of things we see. According to Hebrews 11:3, the spiritual realm (things that are not seen) created the physical realm (things that are visible).

The entire universe was formed at "God's command" (Heb. 11:3, NLT). The pattern of creation in Genesis chapter one took place as follows: "God said…God called… and God saw" (Gen. 1:9–10). God called the universe into existence out of nothing; He declared that it was to be and it was. Speaking words preceded seeing results.

> The spiritual realm created the physical realm; the spiritual realm can change the physical realm.

God made you in His image, to be like Him, and you can follow His example. You can use your words to create your future. Genesis 1:1 states: "In the beginning God created." You can follow the same example in order to create the kind of life you want.

The spiritual realm created the physical realm. Therefore, if the spiritual realm created the physical realm, then the spiritual realm can change the physical realm. God's Word and your re-created spirit represent the spiritual realm. Faith is a product of your re-created spirit, and faith is released when you speak God's Word. It is up to you to release your faith with your words in order to change the course of your life.

FAITH AND WHO YOU ARE IN CHRIST

The creative ability that made everything we can see and everything we cannot see (including everything in heaven and on earth) is found in Christ.

> For by Him all things were created that are in heaven and that are on earth, visible and invisible, whether thrones or dominions or principalities or powers. All things were created through Him and for Him.
>
> —COLOSSIANS 1:16

The word *Him* refers to Jesus. God created everything in the universe through Jesus Christ, the living Word of God. (See John 1:1–3, 14.) The most powerful change agent in all of history was Jesus Christ. Jesus is the reason God's Word is alive and full of power (Heb. 4:12, AMP). Jesus is the Word of power that is upholding and maintaining and propelling the entire universe. (See Hebrews 1:1–3, AMP.) Jesus rose from the dead and He is alive, now seated at the right hand of God.[3] Understanding the present-day ministry of Jesus Christ will help you develop the necessary belief to create the kind of life you want.[4]

> Therefore, holy brethren, partakers of the heavenly calling, consider the Apostle and High Priest of our confession, Christ Jesus.
>
> —HEBREWS 3:1

Jesus is alive at the right hand of God as your High Priest. The high priest in the Old Testament brought the sacrifice to God on behalf of the people. A high priest goes before God on behalf of the people. Jesus went before God on your behalf to secure an eternal redemption for you (Heb. 9:11–12). Now He waits to confirm that redemption in your life through the words you speak.

You can have confidence that the Word of God will work for you because Jesus is the High Priest of your confession, the words you say. If you will put God's Word in your heart and speak it out of your mouth, God will perform His Word on your behalf. Jesus is living today to confirm the words you say when you speak God's Word. You can have confidence in the words you say because every time you say something that agrees with the Word of God, Jesus brings your words before the Father so He can make them good in your life. God, your heavenly Father, is faithful to do what He has promised in His Word.

> So let us seize and hold fast and retain without wavering the hope we cherish and confess and our acknowledgement of it, for He Who promised is reliable (sure) and faithful to His word.
> —HEBREWS 10:23, AMP

The first part of the above verse is your responsibility; you are to maintain your confession of God's Word. The second part of the above verse is God's responsibility; when you continually speak God's Word, God promises you that He is faithful to perform it. God performing His Word in your life starts by accepting God's Word as the source of truth for your life. Your faith becomes effective when you say the same things about yourself that God says about you in His Word.

> That the sharing of your faith may become effective by the acknowledgment of every good thing which is in you in Christ Jesus.
> —PHILEMON 1:6

41

You should verbally acknowledge every good thing that belongs to you in Christ. Start saying the same things about yourself that God says about you. You should continually make a positive confession of who you are, what you have, and what you can do because you are in Christ. Then, act on the "in Him" scriptures in every area of your life. Live your life in accordance with the "in Him" scriptures.

> Your faith becomes effective when you say the same things about yourself that God says about you in His Word.

All the benefits of your inheritance are available, but you must claim them. You claim your inheritance and receive your benefits by confessing (speaking) and then acting (believing) according to what you have spoken. Confess God's Word and act on God's Word to manifest the benefits of your salvation. The promises of God will become a reality in your life when you confess them and act on them.

Verbally confess who you are:

I am a child of God. (Galatians 3:26)

I am a partaker of God's divine nature. (2 Peter 1:4)

I am a new creation. (2 Corinthians 5:17)

I am more than a conqueror. (Romans 8:37)

Verbally confess what you have:

I have eternal life. (1 John 5:11–12)

I have the victory. (1 John 5:4)

I have abundant life. (John 10:10)

I have divine health. (1 Peter 2:24)

I have divine provision. (Philippians 4:19)

Verbally confess what you can do:

I can do all things through Christ who strengthens me. (Philippians 4:13)

I can fulfill God's plan for my life. (Ephesians 2:8–10)

I can live by faith. (2 Corinthians 5:7)

I can walk in love. (1 John 3:14)

I can forgive others. (John 20:23)

I can realize my God-given dream. (John 17:4)

The same Jesus who said you will have whatever you say also told you how you can increase your faith. Your faith can be increased by what you say because faith is released in words.

> And the apostles said to the Lord, "Increase our faith." So the Lord said, "If you have faith as a mustard seed, you can say to this mulberry tree, 'Be pulled up by the roots and be planted in the sea,' and it would obey you."
> —Luke 17:5–6

According to Jesus, with just a little faith, whatever you speak to is going to obey you. You increase your faith by saying the same things that God says in His Word. Instead of talking about what the TV says, instead of talking about what the rest of the world says, instead of talking about what other people are saying, talk about what God says in His Word. God says His plans for you include prosperity, hope, and love. God says He will give you the desires of your heart.

> Jesus is the High Priest of your positive confession of God's Word.

God says He is going to make all your plans succeed. Remain obedient by saying the same thing about your life, your success, your heart's

43

desire, and your God-given dream that God says about them. You can have confidence that what you speak to will obey you because Jesus said so!

> Seeing then that we have a great High Priest who has passed through the heavens, Jesus the Son of God, let us hold fast our confession.
> —HEBREWS 4:14

You can keep your confidence high in the face of contradictory circumstances by holding fast to your confession. You can stay motivated when the evidence of the sense realm suggests that you are not going to receive your heart's desire by holding fast to your confession. You can remain inspired when it looks like your dreams are not going to come true by holding fast to your confession. Keep on saying what God's Word says! This is the essence of faith; continually saying what God says regardless of what is revealed to the senses. You reinforce your faith when you agree with God's Word by speaking it.

Your success in life is going to be measured by the tenacity with which you hold fast to your confession under all circumstances, regardless of whether those circumstances are positive or negative. Jesus said that you will have whatever you say because when you speak faith-filled words of life and blessing, it is Jesus the living Word, who is guaranteeing the efficacy of God's Word. (See Hebrews 7:22, AMP.) When you made Jesus the Lord of your life, He became the High Priest of your positive confession of God's Word.

> Your success in life is going to be measured by the tenacity with which you hold fast to your confession of God's Word.

YOUR WORDS AND YOUR FUTURE

One of the ways you can put your faith into practice is by using your words to paint a picture of the kind of life you want. Your tongue is the brush that paints the portrait of your future.

> My heart is overflowing with a good theme; I recite my composition concerning the King; my tongue is the pen of a ready writer.
>
> —PSALM 45:1

Think of your tongue as the pen that writes the script of the life you desire. You are either speaking your heart's desire or you are speaking the lack of its reality in your life. Your words are either bringing the supernatural power of God into action in your life or keeping God's power idle in your life. Your tongue is the pen that describes with words what your future will look like. Your tongue has in it the power of life and death.

> The tongue has the power of life and death, and those who love it will eat its fruit.
>
> —PROVERBS 18:21, NIV

You decide whether you are going to grow a crop of success or a crop of failure with the words that come out of your mouth. The kind of fruit growing in your life is determined by the words you speak. The fruit you are growing with your words produces the results you are experiencing in your life. Speaking positive words like "I love you" will attract life into your world. Speaking negative words like "I hate you" will attract death into your world.

Speaking your heart's desire would be analogous to speaking words of life. Speaking the evidence of your five senses when it contradicts the realization of your God-given dream would be analogous to speaking words of death. Whether you speak words of life

Speaking God's Word always produces prosperous results!

45

or words of death, you will reap a harvest from your words just as a farmer enjoys the crops he planted. The farmer can only reap from what he plants. You can only reap from what you plant with your words.

Make sure your words are taking you in the right direction. Continue to believe and confess what God says you are. Continue to believe and confess what God says you have. Continue to believe and confess what God says you can do. Continue to believe and confess your heart's desire. Continue to believe and confess your God-given dream.

Your life and your future will be enhanced by or limited by the words that come out of your mouth. The outcomes that will take place in your future will be created by the words that come out of your mouth today. You are responsible for the results your words are producing.

> So shall My word be that goes forth from My mouth; it shall not return to Me void, But it shall accomplish what I please, And it shall prosper in the thing for which I sent it.
>
> —Isaiah 55:11

Living in agreement with God means living in accordance with His Word. When you speak your heart's desire in accordance with God's will, you are agreeing with God. When you are in agreement with God's Word, your life will prosper with the results. You please God when you speak words that produce prosperous results. Speaking God's Word always produces prosperous results!

> You have given him his heart's desire and have not withheld the request of his lips. Selah [pause, and think of that]!
>
> —Psalm 21:2, amp

Pause and think about the responsibility God has taken for you to receive your heart's desire. Your heavenly Father has already made provision for you to realize your God-given dream. Next, pause and think about the responsibility you have to receive your heart's desire and realize your God-given dream. The request of your lips will not be withheld. Your responsibility includes maintaining a positive faith confession concerning your heart's desire and the realization of your God-given dream. Be sure your words remain operative by saying the same thing about you and your life that God says about you and your life.

CHAPTER PRINCIPLES

1. God's will is that the reality of who you are in Christ becomes the dominant desire of your heart.

2. Your heart's desire includes what you have a passion to be, to do, and to have.

3. A successful life is a series of successful days. Your daily habits are creating your future.

4. God gave you His life, His nature, and His ability so that you could tap into the force that created the universe.

5. Jesus came to the earth so you could have and enjoy life, and have it in abundance!

6. Everything you need for the rest of your life has already been provided for you in Christ.

7. Jesus said that you are going to have whatever you believe in your heart and say with your mouth.

8. The principles in God's Master Success Book work in your life as you live in accordance with them.

9. The proof of how motivated you are is revealed by what you do.

10. Faith is the substance that makes what you see out of what you do not see.

11. The spiritual realm created the physical realm; the spiritual realm can change the physical realm.

12. The most powerful change-agent in all of history was Jesus Christ. Jesus is the reason God's Word is alive and full of power.

13. Your faith becomes effective when you say the same things about you and your life that God says about you and your life.

14. You reinforce your faith when you agree with God's Word by speaking it.

15. You can paint a picture of your future with your own words.

16. Speaking God's Word always produces prosperous results!

Chapter 4

YOUR THOUGHTS
RUN YOUR LIFE

MODERN SOCIETY IS very problem conscious. Most people focus on their problems, their trials, and the difficulties in their lives. Dwelling on problems promotes negative thinking and produces negative results. Dwelling on solutions to problems promotes positive thinking and produces positive results. The battle between positive thoughts and negative thoughts takes place in your mind.

The way you think is important because a thought takes place before a word is spoken and Jesus said you will have whatever you say. Words spoken out of a believing heart influence the future events in your life. However, your believing and your speaking are based on your thinking. Therefore, if your thinking is wrong, your believing will be wrong, and if your believing is wrong, then your speaking will be wrong. The way you think begins the process.

> Be careful what you think, because your thoughts run your life.
> —PROVERBS 4:23, NCV

Your life will tend to move in the direction of your dominant thoughts. The way you think is the beginning of future events that will take place in your life. Enjoying life begins with what you do with your thoughts. Overcoming the challenges of life starts when you learn to control your thoughts.

Learning to control your thoughts is an integral step toward tapping into the force that created the universe. The ability of the Creator of the universe is within you. Developing your potential by accessing that ability requires that you control your thoughts. Your victory has already been secured, but enjoying that victory requires that you learn to recognize God's thoughts.

> In the beginning was the Word, and the Word was
> with God, and the Word was God.
>
> —John 1:1

God's Word contains God's will. God's Word contains God's thoughts.[1] Knowing what God thinks about any given matter, and applying that knowledge, moves you toward the enjoyment of a victorious life. Victorious living begins when you tap into the force that created the universe by thinking God's thoughts. What God thinks is found in *God's Master Success Book*.

God's Word contains
God's thoughts.

There are two primary sources from which thoughts are generated. First, the physical realm. What you can see, hear, smell, touch, and taste represent the physical realm. Thoughts are generated from the input of the five physical senses. You see something and a thought is generated, you hear something and a thought is generated, you smell something and a thought is generated, you touch something and a thought is generated, you taste something and a thought is generated. The majority of your thoughts are coming into your mind through your five physical senses. Second, the spiritual realm. God's Word and your re-created spirit represent the spiritual realm. The Word of God shows you what God put in your re-created spirit at the new birth when you became a new creation. You can obtain your thoughts from *God's Master Success Book*. Fill your mind with God's Word and God's thoughts will become your thoughts. Set aside some quiet time each day for your fellowship with God and God's thoughts will become an ever increasing source of your thoughts.

The spiritual battle is between the physical realm (what the five senses indicate) and the spiritual realm (what God's Word says). From the day you were born physically, you were programmed to think according to your five physical senses; but now that you are born again spiritually, you should start thinking according to your re-created spirit.

Thoughts can come into your mind from both the physical realm and the spiritual realm. The direction your thoughts take you is determined by the thoughts

> Tap into the force that created the universe—think God's thoughts!

you allow yourself to entertain. The amount of influence any source of thoughts has on you is determined by how much you permit that source to influence you.

> Casting down arguments and every high thing that exalts itself against the knowledge of God, bringing every thought into captivity to the obedience of Christ.
>
> —2 Corinthians 10:5

It is your responsibility to do something with the thoughts that come into your mind. Any thought that opposes the knowledge of God must be dealt with. You should discard every thought that does not agree with God's new creation picture of you. "Bringing every thought into captivity to the obedience of Christ" means that you are to replace every thought that opposes the truth of God's Word. If a thought does not agree with the Word of God, remove it from your mind; let it go and do not dwell on it. You are to bring your thoughts under your control and make your thoughts conform to the teachings of Christ. You have the ability to think God's thoughts because God gave you the mind of Christ.

> But we have the mind of Christ (the Messiah) and do hold the thoughts (feelings and purposes) of His heart.
>
> —1 CORINTHIANS 2:16, AMP

The mind of Christ will influence your life as you allow God's thoughts to become your thoughts. Your thoughts are to reflect the principles contained in *God's Master Success Book*. An obedient thought life is one that focuses on who you are, what you have, and what you can do because you are in Christ. An obedient thought life allows the Holy Spirit to renew, reeducate, and redirect your thinking. An obedient thought life is one that agrees with your re-created spirit.

> Transformation begins when your mind is brought to the understanding of God's Word.

Everything you need for the rest of your life already exists in your re-created spirit, including the mind of Christ. Manifesting in the physical realm what already exists in your re-created spirit is called living out of your re-created spirit. Once you are born again, the rest of your Christian life is learning how to live out of your re-created spirit.[2] God's thoughts, as outlined in God's Word, currently reside in your re-created spirit. The mind of Christ resides in your re-created spirit.

You are on a mental and spiritual journey. You are on the way to things and things are on their way to you, and it all starts with your thoughts. Promoting healthy positive thoughts requires discipline. One of your daily disciplines should include renewing your mind. Renewing your mind is a process, not a single event. Set aside some time each day to renew your mind by reading and studying *God's Master Success Book*. As you renew your mind with God's Word, you will be better able to control every thought that enters your mind.

> And do not be conformed to this world, but be
> transformed by the renewing of your mind, that
> you may prove what is that good and acceptable
> and perfect will of God.
>
> —ROMANS 12:2

Meditating on God's Word changes the way you think. Let the Holy Spirit transform you by changing the way you think. Transformation takes place when a person with a renewed mind lives according to the good, acceptable, and perfect will of God. The good and acceptable and perfect will of God includes filling your mind with the thoughts that are contained in *God's Master Success Book*.

God's thoughts become your thoughts as you learn who God says you are, what God says you have, and what God says you can do. Old habits of thinking negative, unproductive thoughts get replaced by new habits of thinking positive, productive, God-type thoughts. The more time you spend meditating on God's Word, the sooner the principles in *God's Master Success Book* will become productive in your life. As the principles in *God's Master Success Book* become productive in your life, you will experience transformation.

> The way God changes your thinking is through His Word.

> "For My thoughts are not your thoughts, Nor are
> your ways My ways," says the LORD. "For as the
> heavens are higher than the earth, So are My ways
> higher than your ways, And My thoughts than
> your thoughts."
>
> —ISAIAH 55:8–9

God's thoughts are higher than your thoughts because God operates in the spiritual realm, not the physical realm as we do. Think according to God's Word and you will find yourself living according to God's will. God's thoughts include living in victory, health, and prosperity. When you visualize yourself living in victory, health, and prosperity, you are thinking God-type thoughts.

Whenever you are confronted with a negative situation, get God's counsel on that situation. What God thinks about a particular situation is what you should think about that situation. God can see the before, the during, and the after of your situation. God does not stagger at the challenges that come along. He does not go by whether the situation appears to be getting worse. God goes by the victory He has already secured for you through Jesus Christ. Jesus won the victory for you, and now He is waiting for you to accept and enjoy your victory. The source of information that prevents you from enjoying your victory comes from the sense realm. The sense realm can stimulate your mind into negative thinking or positive thinking. Every situation in your life comes with the choice to entertain negative thoughts or to entertain positive thoughts. Thinking according to God's Word removes the negatives and leaves room for only the positives.

> When you visualize yourself living in victory, health, and prosperity, you are thinking God-type thoughts.

If you continually think about the problems in your life, this pattern of thinking will have a negative impact on the peace and happiness in your life. Conversely, if you think about the solutions to your problems, this pattern of thinking will have a positive impact on the peace and happiness in your life. Holding God-type positive thoughts in your mind, by visualizing solutions to your problems, will result in a significant increase of peace and happiness in your life. Most of the misery that you have experienced in your life was the result of the thoughts you allowed to be entertained in your mind. Negative thoughts can enter your mind at any time, but it is up to you to decide whether you are going to dwell on them. It is up to you whether you will act on those negative thoughts. The biblical response to negative thoughts is to replace negative thoughts with God's thoughts. Replace negative thoughts with the principles found in *God's Master Success Book* and your mind will be filled with the peace of God.

> Don't worry about anything; instead, pray about everything. Tell God what you need, and thank him for all he has done. Then you will experience God's peace, which exceeds anything we can understand. His peace will guard your hearts and minds as you live in Christ Jesus.
> —Philippians 4:6–7, nlt

The cause of worry is dwelling on problems. The cause of anxiety is worrying. Anxiety begins in your mind due to negative thoughts. Anxiety is a negative force that will attract problems into your life. Allowing negative thoughts to remain in your mind causes you to take a journey to the place you fear to go. Anxiety is the opposite of God's peace. God's Word encourages you to exchange anxiety for prayer and thanksgiving. The result of exchanging anxiety for prayer and thanksgiving is God's peace. God's peace is not merely a psychological state of positive thinking; it is an inner tranquility based on peace with God through Jesus Christ (Rom. 5:1). As you live according to who you are in Christ, you will experience peace with God. Peace with God is perfect peace!

> You will keep in perfect peace all who trust in you,
> all whose thoughts are fixed on you!
> —Isaiah 26:3, nlt

The degree to which your mind is filled with God's thoughts is the degree to which you will experience the perfect peace of God. You must keep your mind filled with God's thoughts, not your problems. The battle between peace and anxiety is being waged in your mind. Exchanging anxiety for peace requires you to maintain your trust in God and His Word.

Many people suffer from stress and anxiety because they meditate on failure. Entertaining defeatist thoughts is contrary to God's Word because God has already secured the victory for you. Your thought-life should be characterized by the principles in *God's Master Success Book*.

> Finally, brethren, whatever things are true, whatever things are noble, whatever things are just, whatever things are pure, whatever things are lovely, whatever things are of good report, if there is any virtue and if there is anything praiseworthy—meditate on these things.
>
> —Philippians 4:8

Make a conscious effort to fill your mind with thoughts that are true, honorable, right, pure, lovely, and admirable. Think about things that are excellent and worthy of praise. Keep your mind filled with Philippians 4:8 thoughts!

You can apply the principles in *God's Master Success Book* to your life by replacing negative thought patterns with positive thought patterns. Replace negative thoughts with positive thoughts of who you are in Christ. See yourself the way you want to become. Change the way you think to become what you want to be.

> Change the way you think to become what you want to be.

Your thought patterns determine your ability to break bad habits such as negative thinking. The key to victory over bad habits is refocusing your thoughts, not resisting negative thoughts. Resisting negative thoughts forces you to focus on the very thoughts you are trying to resist. Resisting negative thoughts actually reinforces bad habits. Focusing on any thought, positive or negative, reinforces the related habit. You can break an old bad habit by creating a new good habit. Once your thoughts focus on the new habit, the old habit starts to fade away. Replace your old bad habit caused by negative thoughts with a good habit caused by positive thoughts.

Your mind will always be occupied with thoughts. You can discontinue a thought by replacing it with another thought. Whatever you focus on will tend to increase in your life. The more you think about something, positive or negative, the more the outcome of that thought will be attracted into your life. This new way of positive thinking will allow you to enjoy the victory that God has already provided for you.

The way you think will create the habits that will move you toward the realization of your God-given dream.

1. The battle between positive thoughts and negative thoughts takes place in your mind.

2. Your believing and your speaking are based on your thinking.

3. The way you think is the beginning of future events that will take place in your life.

4. God's Word contains God's thoughts.

5. Victorious living begins when you tap into the force that created the universe by thinking God's thoughts.

6. The direction your life takes is determined by the thoughts you allow yourself to entertain.

7. An obedient thought life is one that focuses on who you are, what you have, and what you can do because you are in Christ.

8. The more time you spend meditating on God's Word, the sooner the principles in *God's Master Success Book* will become productive in your life.

9. Entertaining defeatist thoughts is contrary to God's Word.

10. Jesus won the victory for you, and now He is waiting for you to accept and enjoy your victory.

11. The result of exchanging anxiety for prayer and thanksgiving is God's peace.

12. Change the way you think to become what you want to be.

13. The key to victory over bad habits is refocusing your thoughts, not resisting negative thoughts.

14. You can discontinue a thought by replacing it with another thought.

15. Focusing on any thoughts, positive or negative, reinforces habits.

16. Whatever you focus on will tend to increase in your life.

17. The way you think will create the habits that will move you toward the realization of your God-given dream.

Chapter 5

Living on God's Frequency

WHAT HAPPENS WHEN you try to listen to Christian music on the rock music station? What happens when you try to listen to country music on the jazz station? If you do not tune in to the station you want to listen to, you will not hear what you want to hear. When a station broadcasts on 89.9 but you tune in to 90.1, what you hear from the station is mostly muffled noise. Wrong station or slightly off on your tuning, the end result is about the same; you cannot receive what the station is broadcasting. The problem is that you are on the wrong frequency. The sender is in control of the frequency. If you want to hear the sender's program you must tune in to the correct frequency, the sender's frequency.

God is the sender and you are the receiver. You could be doing everything else right, but if you are not tuned in to God's frequency, you will not be able to receive from God. You must be living on God's frequency to tap into the force that created the universe. God is the sender and He is in control of the frequency. It is your responsibility to adjust your frequency to match God's frequency. God is the same yesterday, today, and tomorrow. God never changes, so that only leaves you. God's frequency is revealed in *God's Master Success Book*.

God's Frequency Is a Love Frequency

> God is love, and all who live in love live in God,
> and God lives in them.
> —1 John 4:16, nlt

Love is God's nature; love is God's frequency. Both the precept and the principle of love point to the Person of God Himself. The degree to which you continue to live in love is the degree to which you continue to live on God's frequency. When you walk in love, you are living on God's frequency.

Walking in love is living on God's frequency.

It is important to understand how the Bible uses the word *love* in the New Testament. The original language of the New Testament is Greek. The Greek language uses different words for different types of love. The Greek word *phileo* and the Greek word *agape* are both translated as *love*. Although *phileo* and *agape* are different Greek words, the English translation for both words is *love*. The Greek word *phileo* refers to natural human love. The Greek word *agape* refers to the God-kind of love.[1]

Natural love is a friendly affection, an emotional response to appreciation for the qualities of a person. The God-kind of love is sacrificial and selfless. Natural love cherishes a person. The God-kind of love values and esteems a person. Natural love gives love when it receives love. The God-kind of love constantly gives love; it is unconditional.

There are significant differences between unconditional love and love that is withheld unless it is also received. Agape love is much deeper than phileo love. Agape love is constant, selfless, and sacrificial. Agape love is given by choice and perceives a sense of value and worth in a person. Agape love is unconditional. Agape love is the God-kind of love.

> Dear friends, let us continue to love one another,
> for love comes from God. Anyone who loves is a
> child of God and knows God. But anyone who
> does not love does not know God, for God is love.
> —1 JOHN 4:7–8, NLT

Love comes from God because God is love. Your re-created spirit has already received the God-kind of love. This agape love that is now within you is meant to be directed toward other people. Agape love promotes cooperation and helps you to get along with other people. Life becomes easier and more productive when you get along with others, and getting along with other people means loving them. Adjust your frequency and enjoy the benefits.

> Agape love, the God-kind of love, is unconditional.

Walking in love, living on God's frequency, will improve your interpersonal relationships. The fundamental concept, "love your neighbor as yourself," is repeated eight times in the Bible.[2]

> For the whole Law [concerning human relation-
> ships] is complied with in the one precept, You
> shall love your neighbor as [you do] yourself.
> —GALATIANS 5:14, AMP

To be effective loving others, the first person you must love is you. The phrase, "as you do yourself" is predicated upon a healthy positive self-image. As a child of God, the basis for your self-esteem is found in knowing who you are in Christ. God chose to have agape love for you. God decided that you are of worth and value, and that you are to be esteemed. Your self-image should reflect the unlimited potential that is yours because the life, nature, and ability of the Creator of the universe reside within you.

The whole law concerning human relationships is summed up in one word: *love*. Love is God's frequency. Living on God's frequency is the key to developing successful human relationships. To enjoy a successful life, you must learn how to be successful in your relationships. Approximately 80 percent of the joy and happiness in life involve other people. Conversely, approximately 80 percent of the pain and anguish in life also involve other people. When you have love for other people, it is much easier to get along with them. Success in life depends upon your ability to get along with other people.

Developing your people skills is one of the most important things you can do to enhance your life. As your people skills improve, getting along with others keeps getting easier. Successfully interacting with other people is one of the greatest challenges you will face, both in your business relationships and in your personal relationships.

> Success in life depends upon your ability to get along with other people.

When you are living on God's frequency, your people skills improve, and then your relationships with other people improve.

Agape love unlocks the solutions to human relationship problems. Love is the key to improving human relationships. When you walk in love, you release the power of God into your life. When you step out of love, you are off of God's frequency and His ability remains idle in your relationships.

> If we love our Christian brothers and sisters, it proves
> that we have passed from death to eternal life.
> —1 John 3:14, nlt

Your love for your brothers and sisters in Christ is proof that you possess eternal life. Love is the inward indicator that assures you of your passage from spiritual death to eternal life. Love is the outward indicator that displays your relationship with God. When you received eternal life, you received the nature of God, and that nature includes agape love.

The entire new covenant is based on love; God's love for us, our love for Him, love toward others, love toward ourselves, and even love for our enemies (Matt. 5:43–44). God would not admonish you to do something that you are not capable of doing. You have the ability to walk in love. You have the ability to live on God's frequency, and that ability can be developed by following the instructions in *God's Master Success Book.*

You Have the Ability to Live on God's Frequency

The confirmation that you have the ability to walk in love comes from knowing that you received the God-kind of love at the new birth. Agape love resides within you because you are a new creation.

> For we know how dearly God loves us, because he
> has given us the Holy Spirit to fill our hearts with
> his love.
> —Romans 5:5, nlt

The Holy Spirit has filled your heart with agape love, and now the role of the Holy Spirit includes helping you manifest that love in your life. You have the ability to give away that which you possess. You possess the God-kind of love, and you have the ability to walk in love toward others.

> But the fruit of the Spirit is love, joy, peace, patience,
> kindness, goodness, faithfulness, gentleness and
> self-control.
> —Galatians 5:22–23, niv

Your re-created spirit is filled with agape love. When the Holy Spirit controls your life, His presence within you produces the God-kind of love in your life. God has given you the ability to walk in love and now you have the opportunity to do it!

> No one has ever seen God. But if we love each
> other, God lives in us, and his love is brought to

63

full expression in us. And God has given us his
Spirit as proof that we live in him and he in us.

—1 John 4:12–13, nlt

You experience God's presence when you walk in love. Other people are able to see an expression of God's presence through you when
you are living on God's frequency. You have the ability to love other
people with the God-kind of love, and that ability is released within
you by the Holy Spirit as you practice living on God's frequency.

Obstacles to Living on God's Frequency

Remove the obstacles to living on God's frequency, and walking in
love is almost automatic.

And we have known and believed the love that
God has for us. God is love, and he who abides in
love abides in God, and God in him.

—1 John 4:16

The first obstacle to living on God's frequency is not knowing
and believing how much God loves you. You must understand the
God-kind of love and believe that God has unconditional love for you
before you can walk in love toward others. Both knowledge *and* belief
are necessary to put the ability to live on God's frequency into practice. You must first accept the love of God personally for yourself.

There is no fear in love. But perfect love drives out
fear, because fear has to do with punishment. The
one who fears is not made perfect in love.

—1 John 4:18, niv

The second obstacle to living on God's frequency is fear. Fear
would be justified if you were not a child of God. You are a child of
God and you have received a new nature filled with eternal life. You
will not be punished, you will be shown grace, undeserved mercy.

You will not receive God's judgment because you have already received God's unconditional love. You are not God's sinful child; you are God's forgiven child!

> If someone says, "I love God," and hates his brother, he is a liar; for he who does not love his brother whom he has seen, how can he love God whom he has not seen? And this commandment we have from Him: that he who loves God must love his brother also.
>
> —1 John 4:20–21

The third obstacle to living on God's frequency is not walking in love. You prove your love for God by loving others. When you hurt others, you are hurting God. The next time you are tempted to say something bad about someone or do something bad to someone, ask yourself, "Do I really want to do this to God?" That question and your answer are powerful incentives to encourage you to choose a course of action that shows love toward others.

Developing the Ability to Live on God's Frequency

You have the God-kind of love, agape love, within you. The God-kind of love gives you the ability to love others. However, that ability needs to be developed. You can develop your ability to walk in love by understanding the characteristics of the God-kind of love and then practicing those characteristics. The characteristics of the God-kind of love are found in 1 Corinthians chapter thirteen. The thirteenth chapter of 1 Corinthians is commonly referred to as the love chapter.

> You experience God's power when you walk in love.

> Love endures long and is patient and kind; Love never is envious nor boils over with jealousy, is not boastful or vainglorious, does not display itself haughtily. It is not conceited (arrogant and inflated with pride); it is not rude (unmannerly), and does not act unbecomingly. Love (God's love in us) does not insist on its own rights or its own way, for it is not self-seeking; it is not touchy or fretful or resentful; it takes no account of the evil done to it [it pays no attention to a suffered wrong]. It does not rejoice at injustice and unrighteousness, but rejoices when right and truth prevail. Love bears up under anything and everything that comes, is ever ready to believe the best of every person, its hopes are fadeless under all circumstances and it endures everything [without weakening]. Love never fails [never fades out or becomes obsolete or comes to an end].
>
> —1 CORINTHIANS 13:4–8, AMP

The characteristics of agape love are descriptive of God because God is love. These characteristics are part of who God is. This is God's frequency, the love frequency. These characteristics also reflect God's attitude. Your attitude toward others should reflect God's attitude toward you. Attitude influences behavior. Your behavior should reflect the God-kind of love. You are living on God's frequency when your attitude and your behavior reflect the characteristics of the God-kind of love.

> You are living on God's frequency when your attitude and your behavior reflect the characteristics of the God-kind of love.

Love endures long and is patient and kind

Your patience with yourself and others is indicated by the amount of complaining you do while you are in the process of realizing your God-given dream. Patience endures without complaining. Sometimes people have no choice but to endure, but they are neither patient nor kind along the way. Persevere and remain kind toward others even during the difficult times in your life.

Love never is envious nor boils over with jealousy

Both envy and jealousy will prevent you from tuning in to God's frequency. Envy and jealousy are different but related. Envy desires to deprive another of what he has. Jealousy craves to have the same or the same sort of thing for itself. Envy and jealousy are both filled with resentment over the advantages, possessions, or attainments of someone else. Envy and jealousy are detrimental to your success and either one will inhibit the realization of your God-given dream.

Love is not boastful or vainglorious, does not display itself haughtily

An inflated ego flaunts its own perceived excellence. Those who consider themselves better than others only fool themselves. Bragging about possessions or achievements will not impress others, but it will make an impression on them, albeit a negative one. A good impression is made by following the example that was provided by Jesus. Walk in love; that is what will please God.

Love is not conceited, arrogant, and inflated with pride

People who overly value their own importance appear to others as being arrogant and conceited. People who are full of pride tend to base their worth on what they have and what they do. Your source of worth should not come solely from people. Your source of worth should come first from God.

Your worth has already been established by who God says you are. You are a child of God. Your worth and value are based on God's love for you. Your relationship with God is the basis of your worth.

Love is not rude, unmannerly, and does not act unbecomingly

Bad manners offend others. Rude behavior insults others. Courtesy and polite behavior both show respect for others. Unbecoming people rarely care about manners and usually have little concern for saying "please" or "thank you." There is power in a hand-written thank you note. When you exhibit good manners you show others the love that is within you.

Love does not insist on its own rights or its own way; it is not self-seeking

Love does not attempt to force its preferences on others. Love does not manipulate attention to itself. Love is charitable and takes an interest in other people. Love maintains a generous, giving attitude.

Love is not touchy or fretful or resentful.

People who are touchy, fretful, or resentful are easily irritated and quick to express their displeasure. Love is not critical and does not get upset easily. Love is even-tempered, good-natured, and accepting of others.

Love takes no account of the evil done to it; it pays no attention to a suffered wrong

Love promotes forgiveness. Forgiving the offenses of others is often the most challenging barrier to success. The reason this barrier is often the most challenging is because it tends to be the most personal. Receiving a personal offense hurts, and retaliation may appear to be justifiable. Your personal situation may involve imperfect parents, physical or emotional abuse, being lied to or about, being cheated out of money, or being disappointed or betrayed by someone you fully trusted. Whatever your personal situation may be, withholding forgiveness has consequences. Forgiveness sets you free from dwelling on past hurts, real or imagined. Forgiveness does not require you to permit continuing abuse or maintain ongoing association. Forgiveness brings freedom from anger, self-pity, and bitterness. Forgiveness allows you to experience peace. Forgiving yourself and others is a key ingredient to success. Forgiveness could be the key that unlocks your full potential.

Love does not rejoice at injustice and unrighteousness, but rejoices when right and truth prevail

Love does the right thing for the right reason. Love does not gossip or take pleasure at the misfortune of others. There is no room in success for a malevolent attitude. Love rejoices when truth and justice prevail.

Love bears up under anything and everything that comes, is ever ready to believe the best of every person, its hopes are fadeless under all circumstances, and it endures everything without weakening

Love does not give up. Love never quits. Love refuses to surrender to failure.

Love believes in people. Love desires to bring out the best in others. Love does not jump to negative conclusions. Love helps others through challenging circumstances. Love inspires others to realize their God-given dreams.

Love overcomes discouragement and frustration with hope for the future. Love provides the strength to successfully go through the trials of life. There is no limit to what you can accomplish when you are motivated by the God-kind of love.

> Living on God's frequency connects you to the source of power that can transform your life.

Love never fails

Love never fails. Love will always succeed. Living on God's frequency connects you to the source of power that can transform your life.

RELEASING THE ABILITY TO LIVE ON GOD'S FREQUENCY

Releasing the ability to live on God's frequency requires action on your part; action that includes speaking, listening to, and practicing the love scriptures.[3] Living on God's frequency, walking in love, will improve your personal, family, and business relationships.

Jesus said that you will have whatever you say (Mark 11:23). Speaking the love scriptures will cause the characteristics of agape love to become a reality in your life. You can personalize the characteristics of the God-kind of love by saying them in the first person. Substitute the word "I" for the word "love." "I endure long and am patient and kind." "I am ever ready to believe the best of every person." "I never fail." Speaking the love scriptures is part of the process that enables you to tap into the force that created the universe.

Listening to the love scriptures helps you tune in to God's frequency.[4] Listening to the love scriptures helps you live on God's frequency by increasing your faith. Faith increases as you hear God's Word, and the love scriptures are part of God's Word. You increase your belief in the love scriptures by hearing them. When you speak you are hearing your own words. When you listen, or speak and listen, to the love scriptures you are acting on God's Word. Results come as you exercise your faith by acting on God's Word.

> God's power becomes effective in your life as you practice living on God's frequency.

Practicing the love scriptures will cause the characteristics of the God-kind of love to manifest in your life. God's power becomes effective in your life as you practice living on God's frequency. Acting on God's Word by practicing the love scriptures releases the power that created the universe. God's power operating in your life gives you the ability to receive your heart's desire and realize your God-given dream.

> And we will receive whatever we request because
> we obey him and do the things that please him.
> —1 JOHN 3:22, NLT

The confidence to receive your heart's desire and realize your God-given dream comes from obeying God and doing the things that please Him. Obeying the instructions in *God's Master Success*

Book includes walking in love, and walking in love is necessary in order to please God.

> Those who obey God's commandments live in fellow-
> ship with him, and he with them. And we know he
> lives in us because the Holy Spirit lives in us.
> —1 JOHN 3:24, NLT

Walking in love and fellowship with God are connected. Walking in love maintains fellowship with God. The Holy Spirit facilitates fellowship with God as He increases your desire to walk in love.

You have free will. You choose whether or not to allow agape love, the God-kind of love, to influence your behavior. Living on God's frequency encourages your success in life because love never fails. Love always succeeds!

You can make dramatic changes in your life during the next thirty days. For the next thirty consecutive days, first thing in the morning and last thing at night, recite the following statements:

Agape love resides in my re-created spirit.

I allow the God-kind of love to influence my
behavior.

I am a kind person who perseveres without
complaining.

I am content as I pursue the realization of my God-
given dream.

I am modest and clothed with humility.

I maintain a loving attitude that is free from conceit,
arrogance, and pride.

I am polite and courteous.

I act appropriately in every situation.

I am tolerant and show respect for other people.

I am a generous giving person.

I am calm and even-tempered.

I release to God all wrongs ever done to me.

I bless those who have hurt me, disappointed me, and let me down.

I tell the truth and stand up for what is right.

I am a winner who continually walks in love.

I believe the best of every person by seeing them the way God sees them.

I have hope for the future no matter what happens.

I stay strong as I am motivated by the God-kind of love.

I succeed when I walk in love because love always succeeds!

CHAPTER PRINCIPLES

1. You must be living on God's frequency in order to tap into the force that created the universe.

2. Love is God's nature; love is God's frequency.

3. When you walk in love, you are living on God's frequency.

4. The God-kind of love is unconditional.

5. When you received eternal life, you received the nature of God, and that nature includes agape love.

6. Getting along with other people means loving them.

7. To be effective loving others, the first person you must love is you.

8. The basis for your self-esteem is found in knowing who you are in Christ.

9. Living on God's frequency is the key to developing successful human relationships.

10. Success in life depends upon your ability to get along with other people.

11. When you walk in love, you release the power of God into your life.

12. When you step out of love, you are off of God's frequency and His ability remains idle in your life.

13. You experience God's presence when you walk in love.

14. The ability to love other people is released by the Holy Spirit as you practice living on God's frequency.

15. You prove your love for God by loving others.

16. You are living on God's frequency when your attitude and your behavior reflect the characteristics of the God-kind of love.

17. Love promotes forgiveness. A lack of forgiveness hurts you and prevents you from reaching your full potential.

18. Love inspires others to realize their God-given dreams.

19. God's power becomes effective in your life as you practice living on God's frequency.

20. Walking in love is necessary in order to please God.

Chapter 6

How to be Successful in Life

Everyone has a desire to be successful in life. Whether it is succeeding at work, at school, or in personal relationships, everyone wants to be successful. The Old Testament book of Joshua contains principles that reveal how to be successful in all areas of life. God told Joshua how to be prosperous and successful. The success principles God gave to Joshua will also work for you when you apply them to your life.

> Be strong and courageous, for you are the one who will lead these people to possess all the land I swore to their ancestors I would give them. Be strong and very courageous. Be careful to obey all the instructions Moses gave you. Do not deviate from them, turning either to the right or to the left. Then you will be successful in everything you do. Study this Book of Instruction continually. Meditate on it day and night so you will be sure to obey everything written in it. Only then will you prosper and succeed in all you do. This is my command—be strong and courageous! Do not be

afraid or discouraged. For the LORD your God is
with you wherever you go.

—Joshua 1:6–9, NLT

The presence of God brings the blessing of God. When the Lord
is with someone the Lord's blessing is usually visible. Two of the
indicators of the Lord's blessing are prosperity and success. You can
be confident because the Lord is with you. Wherever you go, you
can be strong and courageous because the presence and power of
God are within you.

> The presence of God brings
> the blessing of God!

Being strong and courageous
is so important that it is repeated
three times, once in verse six,
once in verse seven, and once
in verse nine. Being strong and
courageous equates to being persistent and consistent toward the
realization of your God-given dream. The confidence to be strong
and courageous comes from knowing that God has provided a way
for you to become prosperous and successful.

The phrases "Be careful to obey" in verse seven and "be sure
to obey" in verse eight indicate that success requires action. Success in life is not unconditionally guaranteed. You are responsible for
the realization of your God-given dream. Realizing your God-given
dream will require more than action, it will require persistent and
consistent action. After taking action, your prosperity and success
will require persistence and determination.[1] There is power in perseverance; never give up!

PROSPERITY AND SUCCESS DEFINED

Prosperity is having enough of God's resources to realize your
God-given dream. Prosperity is not necessarily an amount, but the
provision that is received each day as you need it. Success is making measurable progress toward the realization of your God-given

dream. Success is not solely the end result of achieving your goals, but making measurable progress toward achieving your goals.

Success is not measured by how well you do compared to how well someone else does. Success is measured by how well you do compared to your own potential. If you have the potential to earn one million dollars and you earn only one hundred thousand dollars, you have failed to reach your potential. If you have the potential to earn thirty thousand dollars and you earn thirty thousand dollars or more, you have succeeded in reaching your potential. The satisfaction and fulfillment you experience from your success are directly related to your progress versus your potential. The person you become during the journey of life is an integral part of achieving your goals and realizing your God-given dream.[2]

> Prosperity is having enough of God's resources to realize your God-given dream.

One of the best ways to develop a pattern of success is by setting and achieving one small goal after another. Setting and achieving goals develops a pattern of accomplishment. Patterns of accomplishment establish habits, habit-patterns of accomplishment. As a result of establishing habit-patterns of accomplishment, you will have programmed yourself with the thoughts, disciplines, and activities that are involved with accomplishing your goal. Establishing and maintaining habit-patterns of accomplishment program you for success. You will be able to achieve one worthwhile goal after another for the rest of your life.

> Study this Book of Instruction continually. Meditate on it day and night so you will be sure to obey everything written in it. Only then will you prosper and succeed in all you do.
> —Joshua 1:8, NLT

The word *continually* and the phrase *day and night* mean you are to focus on the principles in *God's Master Success Book* on a daily basis. You are responsible for your prosperity, your success, and the realization of your God-given dream. It is up to you to do something if you are going to be successful. Often while you are waiting for God to do something, God is actually waiting for you to do something.

God is waiting for you to do three things. There are three success principles in Joshua 1:8 that will enable and empower you to prosper and succeed in all that you do:

1. Study God's success principles: "Study this Book of Instruction continually."

2. Meditate on God's success principles: "Meditate on it day and night."

3. Practice God's success principles: "Be sure to obey everything written in it."

1. Study God's success principles.

The first principle is to study the instructions contained in *God's Master Success Book*. Studying God's Word is the starting point for your success in life. To become prosperous and successful, study God's Word.[3]

> Success is making measurable progress toward the realization of your God-given dream.

You have available to you the success principles found in the Old Testament and the success principles in the New Testament. The New Testament success principles are found in the Gospels, the Acts of the Apostles, the Epistles, and in the book of Revelation. All of the Epistles were accepted as being for the benefit of the church as a whole, of which you are a part. The success principles in the Epistles include the love scriptures and the "in Him" scriptures.

> Do not let this Book of the Law depart from your mouth.
>
> —Joshua 1:8, niv

To empower your success, combine your study of God's success principles with speaking God's success principles. Speaking God's Word releases the power in God's Word. Focus on speaking the love scriptures and the "in Him" scriptures. Speak three things: who God says you are, what God says you have, and what God says you can do. Studying and speaking the love scriptures and the "in Him" scriptures will give you a good start on the road to prosperity and success.

2. Meditate on God's success principles.

The second principle is to meditate on the instructions contained in *God's Master Success Book*. To become prosperous and successful, meditate on God's Word. Meditating on God's Word will help you internalize God's success principles.[4]

Keep the success principles found in *God's Master Success Book* in the forefront of your mind. To prosper and be successful, meditate on the scriptures that address the issues you are currently working on.

> Blessed is the man
> Who walks not in the counsel of the ungodly,
> Nor stands in the path of sinners,
> Nor sits in the seat of the scornful;
> But his delight is in the law of the LORD,
> And in His law he meditates day and night.
> He shall be like a tree
> Planted by the rivers of water,
> That brings forth its fruit in its season,
> Whose leaf also shall not wither;
> And whatever he does shall prosper.
> —PSALM 1:1–3

Your associations are a major source of your meditation. The people you associate with provide you with a source of information that you will meditate on because you are listening to what they have to say. Who and what you listen to is what you meditate on. The highest and best possible association is with God. When you meditate on God's Word, you are associating with the Creator of the universe. When you meditate on God's Word, you are programming yourself with the success principles contained in *God's Master Success Book*.[5]

3. Practice God's success principles.

The third principle is to practice the instructions contained in *God's Master Success Book*. To become prosperous and successful, practice God's Word. Until you act, God lies dormant. Action brings God on the scene. Success is based on obedience to the will of God. The successful person is the one who seeks God's will and delights in doing what God says in His Word.

> Who and what you listen to is what you meditate on.

Practicing God's Word with diligent obedience causes the blessings of God to overtake you. The Old Testament book of Deuteronomy, written by Moses, contains many of the success principles that Joshua was to study, speak, meditate, and practice in order to prosper and be successful.

> Now it shall come to pass, if you diligently obey the voice of the LORD your God, to observe carefully all His commandments which I command you today, that the LORD your God will set you high above all nations of the earth. And all these blessings shall come upon you and overtake you, because you obey the voice of the LORD your God.
>
> —DEUTERONOMY 28:1–2

It is one thing to be above, but it is quite another for God to set you *high* above. It is one thing to receive the blessings of God into your life, but it is quite another for those blessings to come upon you and overtake you. The prerequisite for these blessings to occur is presented as an opportunity, as indicated by the word *if* in Deuteronomy 28:1. Seizing opportunities effectively requires diligent obedience to the voice of the Lord. God's voice is heard through His Word. To obey God's voice is to obey God's Word. You enable success in your life when you seize the opportunity to not only hear God's Word, but to obey God by putting His Word into practice.

> Practicing God's Word causes the blessings of God to overtake you.

The love scriptures and the "in Him" scriptures give you an excellent starting point for studying, speaking, meditating, and practicing God's Word. When you diligently obey and carefully observe the love scriptures and the "in Him" scriptures, blessings will come upon you and overtake you. God's idea of success is that the blessings overtake you!

PROSPERITY AND SUCCESS INCLUDE INCREASE AND ABUNDANCE

God is a believer in prosperity and success. Prosperity and success include increase and abundance.

> Now so it was, as the multitude pressed about Him to hear the word of God, that He stood by the Lake of Gennesaret, and saw two boats standing by the lake; but the fisherman had gone from them and were washing their nets. Then He got into one of the boats, which was Simon's, and asked him to put out a little from the land. And He sat down and taught the multitudes from the boat. Now when He had stopped speaking, He said to Simon, "Launch out into the deep and let down your nets for a catch." But Simon answered and

said to Him, "Master, we have toiled all night and caught nothing; nevertheless at Your word I will let down the net." And when they had done this, they caught a great number of fish, and their net was breaking. So they signaled to their partners in the other boat to come and help them. And they came and filled both the boats, so that they began to sink.

—Luke 5:1–7

So many people had come to hear Jesus speak that Jesus had to sit in a boat away from the shore so everyone could see and hear him. A multitude of people heard what Jesus said, saw what Jesus did, and witnessed the series of events that followed. Simon (Peter)[6] had worked very hard during the prior night; he was exhausted, and he had caught nothing. When Jesus told Peter to let down his net, Peter, although exhausted, acted on God's Word (the instructions of Jesus). Peter and his partners caught so many fish that they needed a second boat to handle the catch. This display of God's abundance was done openly. Peter and his partners followed God's instructions and the blessings of God overtook them. All those present were shown that God is a God of prosperity and success, increase and abundance. Prosperity and success here are synonymous with increase and abundance.

Occasionally you may find yourself lacking accomplishment, similar to Peter's situation in verse five above. It may appear to you that you are doing everything right. You may be walking in love and living the "in Him" scriptures, but your circumstances may still look bleak. However, you are instructed not to live by what you see, not to live by what you feel, and not to live by the confinement of your present circumstances.

We live by faith, not by sight.

—2 Corinthians 5:7, niv

You are admonished in *God's Master Success Book* to live by faith. Living by faith means doing what God says in His Word and trusting Him to take care of the rest. Trust God to bring the desired results into your life. You are a child of God and you are to live by faith. Your instructions come from God's Word, and you are to be obedient to those instructions. Take command of your circumstances by correctly using the words that come out of your mouth.

The words of Jesus tell you the impact your words will have on your success. You will have what Jesus said you would have; whatever you say (Mark 11:23). The challenge that plagues many people is that they are bellyaching, complaining, and murmuring about one thing or another while they blame God and everyone else for the problems in their life. Instead of blaming, take full responsibility for your success in life by controlling your words. You should always agree with God by speaking prosperity and success over your own life.

Another example of increase and abundance took place shortly after the resurrection of Jesus. (See John 21:1–11.) Jesus appeared to some of His disciples while they were fishing. Once again, the disciples had been out fishing all night and had caught nothing. The next morning Jesus appeared to the disciples and told them to cast their net on the right side of the boat. The disciples acted on God's Word and caught a multitude of large fish.

> Agree with God—speak prosperity and success.

At first, the disciples did not know that it was Jesus who spoke to them, but as a result of catching a multitude of fish they recognized that it was Jesus (who spoke to them). The presence of God (Jesus) brought the blessing of God. Wherever Jesus was, prosperity and success were there. Wherever Jesus went, increase and abundance followed. Supernatural results like those experienced by the disciples can still be experienced in the lives of the modern-day disciples.[7]

God's will for your life includes prosperity and success. You can receive the blessings of prosperity and success into your life by acting on the principles contained in *God's Master Success Book*.

1. The presence of God brings the blessing of God.

2. You are going to have to take continual action to realize your God-given dream.

3. There is power in perseverance; never give up!

4. Prosperity is having enough of God's resources to realize your God-given dream.

5. Success is making measurable progress toward the realization of your God-given dream.

6. The person you become on the journey to success is more important than the end result of reaching your goal.

7. Often while you are waiting for God to do something, God is actually waiting for you to do something.

8. Studying God's Word is the starting point for your success.

9. Speaking God's Word releases the power in God's Word.

10. Meditating on God's Word will help you internalize God's success principles.

11. Your reference group, the people you spend time with, will be one of the most influential factors in determining your success in life.

12. Practicing God's Word with diligent obedience causes the blessings of God to overtake you.

13. The love scriptures and the "in Him" scriptures give you an excellent starting point for studying, speaking, meditating, and practicing God's Word.

14. Living by faith means doing what God says in His Word and trusting Him to bring the desired results into your life.

15. Agree with God by speaking prosperity and success over your own life.

16. You can receive the blessings of prosperity and success into your life by acting on the principles contained in *God's Master Success Book*.

Chapter 7

PROGRAMMING YOUR
SUCCESS MECHANISM

IN ORDER TO be successful in life, it is important to understand your success mechanism—the part of you that produces success. Some success philosophers say your success mechanism is your mind. Some success philosophers say it is your subconscious mind. Other success philosophers say it is a combination of your mind and your subconscious mind. The way you think does have a huge influence on your success in life. However, your success does not solely begin and end with your mind.

Many books have been written on the subject of success, and most of them deal with man on two dimensions, physical and mental.[1] There is one book that surpasses all the others on the subject of success. The ultimate success book is *God's Master Success Book*, the Holy Bible. *God's Master Success Book* identifies your success mechanism and provides the instructions necessary to program your success mechanism.

God's Master Success Book identifies man on three dimensions. *God's Master Success Book* includes the physical and mental dimensions of man, and additionally includes one more dimension, the spiritual dimension. The three-dimensional approach found in *God's*

Master Success Book provides a fuller and more complete understanding of your success mechanism and how you can program it. This three-dimensional approach is much more comprehensive and much more effective than a two-dimensional approach.[2] To effectively program your success mechanism, follow the programming instructions from the Creator of the universe.

> Now may the God of peace Himself sanctify you completely; and may your whole spirit, soul, and body be preserved blameless at the coming of our Lord Jesus Christ.
>
> —1 Thessalonians 5:23

Man is an eternal spirit, he possesses a soul, and he lives in a physical body. *God's Master Success Book* refers to the whole person as containing three distinguishable sets of characteristics:

1. Spirit—The *spirit* is the life principle bestowed on man by God.[3] It is the reflection of the image and likeness of God. The spirit is the part of man that communicates directly with God.

> Your success mechanism is how your spirit, soul, and body are influenced by the condition of your heart.

2. Soul—The *soul* is the immaterial invisible part of man's existence that gives individuality to each person; it is what makes you, you! It is the sentient (conscious) element in man. While the spirit is the life principle bestowed on man by God, the soul is the resulting life constituted as an individual.[4] Soul and spirit are linked to each other, but are plainly distinguished from each other.

3. Body—The *body* is the physical body man lives in while he is here on earth.

There is one other aspect of man, a grouping of characteristics and functions that is essential to the success mechanism, the biblical heart:

Heart—The *heart* is a metaphor for the core self, the inner being of man, the man himself. As such, it is the fountain of all he does.[5] The heart is the innermost spring of personal life; the source of all thoughts and plans, attitudes and desires, motives and choices. The heart is the source and deep seat of the intellect, emotions, and will. It is the center of cognitive and imaginative processes. The heart is the inner part of a person's being where decisions, obedience, intentionality, and devotion are formed. A person's character is determined by the condition of his or her heart.

> Keep your heart with all diligence, For out of it spring the issues of life.
> —Proverbs 4:23

You keep your heart with all diligence by controlling the thoughts that continually occupy your mind. Control the door to your heart and the outcomes (issues) in your life will tend to be positive. Whatever you permit to go through that doorway will eventually be incorporated into programming your success mechanism. Your success mechanism is how your spirit, soul, and body are influenced by the condition of your heart.

The condition of your heart is extremely important to your success. You are to "keep" your heart, diligently guard and protect it. The condition of your heart is instrumental to your success in life, for out of the heart spring the issues of life. The condition of your heart affects everything you do. Your heart is facilitating the results, or lack thereof, that you are experiencing in your life. Guard your heart, for it determines the course of your life.

Your re-created spirit has within it the same creative ability that created the universe. The Holy Spirit within you is available any time you need creative assistance. The Holy Spirit will teach

> God living in you is your connection to the Creator of everything.

you how to use your creative ability. You can use your creative ability to program your success mechanism. When you make a regular confession of your identity as a child of God (who you are, what you have, and what you can do), you are confirming that God's ability is at your disposal, and you are reinforcing your success mechanism.

Effectively programming your success mechanism requires communication with God. God is a spiritual Being (John 4:24, AMP). To effectively communicate with God, to have meaningful fellowship with God, requires a spiritual connection. God leads you and guides you through the indwelling presence of the Holy Spirit.

The shortcoming with most success literature is that most success literature has left out the dimension of man from which all communication with God flows, the spirit of man. Without including consideration for the spiritual dimension, the best that can be done is to address the shadow of the substance rather than the substance itself. You can be effective using only the shadow, your conscious and subconscious mind, to achieve success. However, you will be far more effective when you directly address the substance, your entire success mechanism, to achieve success.

You can learn how to program your success mechanism by studying one of Jesus' parables.[6] In the parable of the sower, Jesus uses an analogy to show what preparations are required to produce positive results in life. Producing positive results in your life requires that you prepare your heart to receive the truth contained in God's Word. In Mark 4:13, Jesus had finished teaching the parable of the sower to a large crowd and He was now alone. Jesus' disciples came to Him and asked Him to explain the parable to them.

> And He said to them, "Do you not understand this parable? How then will you understand all the parables? The sower sows the word. And these are the ones by the wayside where the word is sown. When they hear, Satan comes immediately and takes away the word that was sown in their hearts. These likewise are the ones sown on stony ground who, when they hear the word, immediately receive it with gladness; and they have no root in

themselves, and so endure only for a time. Afterward, when tribulation or persecution arises for the word's sake, immediately they stumble. Now these are the ones sown among thorns; they are the ones who hear the word, and the cares of this world, the deceitfulness of riches, and the desires for other things entering in choke the word, and it becomes unfruitful. But these are the ones sown on good ground, those who hear the word, accept it, and bear fruit: some thirtyfold, some sixty, and some a hundred."

—MARK 4:13–20

The parable of the sower illustrates that after investigating the truth found in God's Word, people fall into one of four groups. The same four groupings apply to those who pursue the principles contained in *God's Master Success Book*. Each group represented in the parable responded differently depending upon the condition of their heart.

Verse 14 states, "The sower sows the word." The seed sown is the truth contained in God's Word. Verse 15 states where the Word of God is sown—in your heart! Your heart is the part of you that facilitates the results in your life. That which you permit into your heart programs your success mechanism.

> Your heart is the part of you that facilitates the results in your life.

The greater your understanding of this parable, the easier it will be for you to program your success mechanism. Three important points will add to your understanding and effectiveness:

1. This parable makes the analogy of the heart being like the ground. If the ground is prepared properly, the seed sown produces an abundant harvest. When your heart is free of rocks, weeds, and thorns, it will facilitate positive results in

your life. Taking action with a prepared heart will cause the power of God to move on your behalf. When that happens, you receive major assistance as you move toward the realization of your God-given dream.

2. The ground does not distinguish between various seeds. The ground produces whatever gets planted. If a farmer plants nightshade, a deadly poison, the ground will produce nightshade. If a farmer plants corn, the ground will produce corn. Your heart does not distinguish between the various seeds (concepts, principles, and ideas) that you plant in it. Your heart will return to you an abundance of whatever you plant, but your heart does not distinguish between the various seeds (concepts, principles, and ideas) that you plant. It is your responsibility to plant a good crop. If you plant a good crop, your heart will produce positive results in your life. Apply the principles in *God's Master Success Book* and your heart will produce success for you. Your abundant harvest waits for you to plant in your heart the success principles found in God's Word.

3. There are four possible groups of people and every individual falls into one of these four groups. Only one of the groups produces lasting results.

Jesus refers to four distinct groups of people in this parable:

Group 1: Those by the wayside where God's Word was sown (Mark 4:15).

Group 2: Those on stony ground where God's Word was sown (Mark 4:16).

Group 3: Those among thorns where God's Word was sown (Mark 4:18).

Group 4: Those on good ground where God's Word was sown (Mark 4:20).

Group 1:
Those by the wayside where God's Word was sown

The first group heard God's Word, but Satan came immediately and took away the truth that was sown in their hearts. Satan is the god of this evil world, and he attempts to keep people from being successful. One of the ways he attempts to do this is by blinding the minds of people so that they cannot receive the truth from God's Word. Therefore, these people are unable to embrace God's success principles.

> Satan, the god of this evil world, has blinded the minds of those who don't believe, so they are unable to see the glorious light of the Good News that is shining upon them. They don't understand the message we preach about the glory of Christ, who is the exact likeness of God.
>
> —2 Corinthians 4:4, nlt

The mind-set of the world is predominantly negative. The negative downward pull of life requires no effort to get sucked into; it is almost automatic. You can learn how to succeed by finding out what God, the Author of success, tells you to do in order to be successful.

You are provided with the principles that will cause you to prosper and be successful in life (Josh. 1:8). It is your responsibility whether or not you succeed or fail in life. You are the one who makes your way prosperous and successful; it is your responsibility! It takes effort to learn and speak God's Word, but it takes very little effort to gossip, speak ill of, and criticize others. It takes a disciplined effort to set aside time each day to study God's Word, but it takes very little effort to sit in front of a

> The ground does not distinguish between crops and weeds; it grows what is planted. Your heart does not distinguish between success and failure; it grows what is planted.

television. It takes effort to act on God's Word in the face of contradictory circumstances, but it takes very little effort to simply accept what the five physical senses are telling you. It takes very little effort to react to life, but it takes self-discipline to respond to life. It takes no effort to fail, just do what the majority of people are doing and the negative downward pull of life will hold you in bondage to a life of mediocrity. Satan is the god of this evil world, and mediocrity is the best he has to offer.

Those in group one put little or no effort into pursuing the principles contained in *God's Master Success Book*, and they receive little or no benefit from God's Word.

Group 2:
Those on stony ground where God's Word was sown

The second group heard God's Word and received it with gladness, but there were some stones in their hearts. When there are

> It takes very little effort to react to life, but it takes self-discipline to respond to life.

stones in your heart, what you plant does not get rooted deeply enough. The roots hit the stones and do not go down deeply enough to produce lasting results. The height of the crop is determined by the depth of its roots. The truth contained in God's Word did not become a way of life for the second group. It takes time to prepare and develop good ground. Everything that is worthwhile in life takes time to develop.

> We know that we are of God, and the whole world lies under the sway of the wicked one.
> —1 John 5:19

> Be sober, be vigilant; because your adversary the devil walks about like a roaring lion, seeking whom he may devour.
> —1 Peter 5:8

There is a negative force operating in this world. The Bible clearly states that Satan is the god of this evil world. Look around you; look at all the heartache, suffering, and violence that exist in the world. You do not need to be a biblical scholar or a genius to figure out that some of the things happening in this world did not come from God. As a child of God, you are in the world, but you do not have to succumb to the world's negative influence. Notice that 1 Peter 5:8 uses the words "whom he may devour," not whomever he "chooses" to devour. Your success cannot be taken from you. To lose your success you must give up your success (e.g., negative thinking). Follow the success principles in *God's Master Success Book* and your success will be a lasting success.

Another problem with the second group is that they are walking by sight, not living by faith. They are living solely by what the five physical senses are indicating. They are reacting to life, not responding to life. Whenever something happens that looks like a problem in their life, they have a tendency to focus on the problem instead of the solution. The people in this group stumble because they lack knowledge (Hosea 4:6). These people heard only a small portion of God's Word. These people had the success principles available to them and chose not to learn more about them. This group of people is well-known for wanting to know: "Why did God do this to me?" The people in this group are their own worst enemies due to their refusal to gain more knowledge.

The second group discovers the truth of God's Word; they find out they have the victory (1 Cor. 15:57), they find out they are the righteousness of God in Christ (2 Cor. 5:21), and they find out they can do all things through Christ who strengthens them (Phil. 4:13). However, when faced with the challenges of life, they either give up easily or give up and blame God. These people lack the courage of their conviction due to their limited knowledge. The "never give up" attitude they were instructed to develop never replaced their old attitude of "give up and blame God."

Those in group two do not make the sustained effort to gain sufficient knowledge by consistently applying the principles contained in *God's Master Success Book*, and they do not receive much benefit from God's Word.

Group 3:
Those among thorns where God's Word was sown

The third group heard God's Word, but it was sown among thorns. There are three thorns that are identified. The first thorn is the cares of this world. The second thorn is the deceitfulness of riches. The third thorn is the desire for other things.

The first thorn consists of the cares, anxieties, worries, and concerns of this world. *God's Master Success Book* gives the solution to worry and anxiety problems:

> Do not fret or have any anxiety about anything.
> —Philippians 4:6, amp

> Casting the whole of your care [all your anxieties, all your worries, all your concerns, once and for all] on Him, for He cares for you affectionately and cares about you watchfully.
> —1 Peter 5:7, amp

You are to take action regarding your cares and anxieties; you are to give them to God. If you hold on to the cares and anxieties of this world, then God does not have them and you get to keep them! When you keep your cares and anxieties, you have disobeyed God because you are admonished to cast all your cares on Him. The reason you can confidently cast your cares on God is because He cares about you affectionately and watchfully. When you cast your burdens on Him by refusing to live in worry, your faith confirms that He will sustain you.

> Cast your burden on the Lord, And He shall sustain you; He shall never permit the righteous to be moved.
> —Psalm 55:22

Instead of worrying, spend that time meditating on the principles contained in *God's Master Success Book*. If you know how to worry, you know how to meditate. Worry is simply meditating on the problems in your life. When worry becomes a habit, every little thing in your life seems to become a burden.

Worry wastes a great deal of time and energy. Worry rarely provides any assistance, but always produces anxiety. Worrying is counterproductive because of the things that people worry about: 40 percent never happen, 30 percent are over and past and cannot be changed, 12 percent are needless health issues, 10 percent are petty miscellaneous worries, and only 8 percent are real legitimate worries. So 92 percent of the average person's worries take up valuable time, cause painful stress, even mental anguish, and are absolutely unnecessary.[7]

You can cause yourself to needlessly live a miserable life by not doing what God has told you to do. God told you to cast your cares, anxieties, worries, concerns, and burdens on Him; do it! Whatever you allow into in your heart programs your success mechanism. Whatever you retain in your heart will eventually come out as results, benefits, or consequences. You cannot retain your burdens and program your heart for success. You will have to choose between burdens and success.

The second thorn is the deceitfulness of riches; the lure, seduction, and temptation of wealth. The people in this group are fooled by the desire to get rich quick. They are deceived because they do not know the difference between what they need and what they want. They may have all they need to live comfortably, but they let themselves become anxious and discontent over what they merely want. This confused condition is the result of the love of money.

> People who want to get rich fall into temptation
> and a trap and into many foolish and harmful
> desires that plunge men into ruin and destruction.
> For the love of money is a root of all kinds of evil.

> Some people, eager for money, have wandered from
> the faith and pierced themselves with many griefs.
> —1 Timothy 6:9–10, niv

Money is *not* the root of all evil. It is the *love of money* that is *a* root of all kinds of evil. When money becomes your love, it becomes a root of evil in your life. When money becomes your love, money becomes your master and it becomes the god that you are serving.

> No one can serve two masters. For you will hate
> one and love the other; you will be devoted to one
> and despise the other. You cannot serve both God
> and money.
> —Matthew 6:24, nlt

The love of money has a debasing influence. You cannot serve both God and money, and serve means love. You can have a large amount of both God and money, but you cannot love them both. When you harbor a love of money, the outcome will be an expression of greed. Your successes will be shallow at best, and will be potentially devastating to the lives of those you love.[8]

The third thorn is the desire for other things; the craving for worldly goods and worldly ways, frivolous pride in possessions and achievements, selfish desires, greedy imaginings, and all the vanity that is inherent in the natural man. These desires inhibit the positive programming of your success mechanism.

> You can have a large amount of both God and money, but you cannot love them both.

Maintaining a balanced outlook is essential to your success. The desire for other things prevents a healthy balanced perspective. Negative emotions, negative thoughts, and negative mental images must be avoided. Mental images and emotional thoughts, positive or negative, when held in your heart, program your success mechanism. An image of someone else's success adds a little success to yourself, while an image of someone else's failure only serves to add a little failure to yourself.

Those in group three are distracted by certain aspects of their own physical existence, and they miss out on the benefits available from God's Word.

Group 4:
Those on good ground where God's Word was sown

The fourth group heard God's Word and accepted it. Those in group four put in the effort to gain knowledge and were proactive in applying that knowledge. They positioned themselves to effectively program their success mechanisms and they received the benefits. The principles in *God's Master Success Book* became their success principles. The benefits contained in God's Word became their benefits.

> And He said to them, Be careful what you are hearing. The measure [of thought and study] you give [to the truth you hear] will be the measure [of virtue and knowledge] that comes back to you—and more [besides] will be given to you who hear.
> —MARK 4:24, AMP

What you hear is a choice. You decide how you want to program your success mechanism by what you choose to hear. What you hear becomes what you meditate on, and what you meditate on goes into your heart and programs your success mechanism. The inevitable result of what you allow into your heart is what eventually comes out of your heart and into your life.

The growth in your life will reflect what you hear and what you meditate on. What you hear and what you meditate on will cause more success to come into your life *or* it will actually cause the success that you have attained to disappear and exit your life. What you hear on a regular basis is the starting point to programming your success mechanism. How you program your success mechanism will ultimately determine the course your life takes. Hearing and accepting God's Word as the source of truth for your life will positively program your success mechanism.

Hearing (and meditating on what you heard) is the basis for building your faith. Faith increases as you hear God's Word. When you meditate on the principles contained in *God's Master Success Book*, you are programming your success mechanism to produce positive results in your life. Programming your success mechanism with God's success principles will allow you to live the life of victory and success that God has made available to you.

> For as he thinks in his heart, so is he.
> —Proverbs 23:7

Notice *God's Master Success Book* does not say, "For as he thinks in his *mind*, so is he." The results you are getting in your life are being produced by the condition of your heart, not solely by the thoughts in your mind. The outcomes in your life flow from your heart.

> Hearing and accepting God's Word as the source of truth for your life will positively program your success mechanism.

What you hear becomes a thought. Your thoughts create images in your mind, and what you meditate on gets stored in your heart. Your heart is being programmed with positive thoughts or negative thoughts. Your heart produces an abundance of whatever you allow to be placed in it. What you mentally accept, feel passion for, and envision in your mind is what gets planted in your heart. The abundance that comes out of your heart reveals your true beliefs, attitudes, and motivation. What is in your heart will come out in your speech and behavior.

> For out of the abundance of the heart his mouth speaks.
> —Luke 6:45

What you allow into your heart influences what comes out in your words. What you speak flows from what is in your heart. What you meditate on programs you to speak in a certain manner. The condition of your heart determines the words you speak and the actions you take. The words you speak and the actions you take are producing the results in your life. Your thoughts and your words will eventually determine how you will act. The eternal truth, spoken by Jesus, is that the content of your heart determines the results that occur in your life.

> A good man out of the good treasure of his heart
> brings forth good things, and an evil man out of
> the evil treasure brings forth evil things.
> —MATTHEW 12:35

Your treasure is the condition of your heart. Store up good things in your heart and your words and actions will be good; your positive results will reflect your input. Store up evil things in your heart and your words and actions will be evil; your negative results will reflect your input. Whatever you store up in your heart, corresponding results will follow.

> Your life is responding to what you think, speak, and do.

The condition of your heart produces the results that occur in your life because the content of your heart determines your thoughts, words, and actions. The production center for the results you are getting in your life is your heart. Program your success mechanism wisely and your production center will produce positive results in your life.

1. *God's Master Success Book* identifies your success mechanism and shows you how to effectively program your success mechanism.

2. Man is an eternal spirit, he possesses a soul, and he lives in a physical body.

3. Your character is determined by the condition of your heart.

4. Your heart is producing the results that you are experiencing in your life.

5. Whatever you permit into your heart programs your success mechanism.

6. Your success mechanism is how your spirit, soul, and body are influenced by the condition of your heart.

7. Taking action with a prepared heart will cause the power of God to move on your behalf.

8. It takes very little effort to react to life, but it takes self-discipline to respond to life.

9. You are to take action regarding your cares and anxieties; you are to give them to God.

10. Money is *not* the root of all evil. It is the *love of money* that is *a* root of all kinds of evil.

11. You can have a large amount of both God and money, but you cannot love them both.

12. Hearing and accepting God's Word as the source of truth for your life will positively program your success mechanism.

13. How you program your success mechanism will ultimately determine the course your life takes.

14. The outcomes in your life flow from your heart.

15. The condition of your heart produces results in your life because the content of your heart determines your thoughts, words, and actions.

16. Your life is responding to what you think, speak, and do.

Chapter 8

THE EMOTIONAL
ROLLER COASTER

EVERYONE HAS TAKEN a ride at one time or another in their life on the emotional roller coaster. You know you are on the emotional roller coaster when the pattern of your life is waking up one day and you are happy and waking up the next day and you are sad. You are on the emotional roller coaster when your life exhibits a series of up and down emotions of happiness and sadness. When you identify the cause of your happiness and the cause of your sadness you will begin the process of minimizing the emotional mood swings you experience. The shorter and fewer the swings, the better off you are. After you have identified the cause of your emotional mood swings, you can seek a solution that will allow you to live your life with more emotional stability.

Happiness and sadness are both states of mind that come and go. The objective is to find out how to be happy all the time. You may have been happy when you graduated from school. You may have been happy when you won a great victory or prize. You may have been happy when you got engaged. You may have been happy when you got married. You may have been happy when you became a parent. During your lifetime many events have made you happy. The problem with these happiness-causing events is that they are transitory, they come and they go. Events come into your life and then they are over; memories are all that remain. When events you expect to happen do not happen, you experience sadness. When you are expecting positive things to happen and they do not happen, then all of a sudden you become sad because the opposite of something that makes you happy is going to make you sad. The antithesis of happiness is sadness.

The term *true happiness* is really a misnomer because the positive events that make you happy are not going to happen all the time. Positive circumstances will not continuously occur in your life; that's just not the way life is.

> He who deals wisely and heeds [God's] word and counsel shall find good, and whoever leans on, trusts in, and is confident in the Lord—happy, blessed, and fortunate is he.
> —PROVERBS 16:20, AMP

God's prescription for happiness is for you to make wise choices based on the principles contained in *God's Master Success Book*. Acting on God's counsel, practicing the principles contained in God's Word, allows you to live a blessed life, which includes happiness.

> Joy is continual happiness.

Your current happiness and your current sadness are states of mind that come and go depending on the circumstances that occur in your life. You can get off the emotional roller coaster by following God's prescription for emotional stability.

The New Testament term for a continual state of happiness is *joy*. Joy originates and emanates from your re-created spirit. When you learn how to grow and release the joy within you, you will be "happy" all the time. Joy is the second fruit of your re-created spirit.

> But the fruit of the Spirit is love, joy, peace, longsuf-
> fering, kindness, goodness, faithfulness, gentleness,
> self-control.
>
> —GALATIANS 5:22–23

Happiness is a state of mind, but joy is a state of being. Happiness is a response to the circumstances of life, but joy is a way
of living. Joy is the happiness you can experience throughout life
regardless of your circumstances. Joy is what allows you to enjoy
happiness through both the good and bad circumstances of life.
When you placed your faith in Christ, you became a new creation,
and one of the characteristics of your new nature is joy. You have the
ability to allow joy to dominate your emotions.

The answers to the following four questions will enable and empower you to get off of the emotional roller coaster:

1. What is joy?
2. Is it God's will for you to live a joyful life?
3. How can you cultivate a joyful life?
4. How does joy grow in your life?

1. What is joy?

Joy is a state of cheerfulness, gladness, and calm delight. A calm
delight is a constant plateau of well-being. Joy is not up one minute
and down the next. Joy is not like
the roller coaster ride of accentuated happiness and accentuated
sadness. Joy is the confidence of
knowing that God has prepared

> Happiness is an emotion. Joy
> is a state of being.

all the paths for your life. Joy is knowing that God has blessed you
with everything you need to live a victorious life. Joy is based on
what God has already done for you through the finished work of
Christ. Joy is based on knowing who you are in Christ.

Joy is characterized by enthusiasm. The word *enthusiasm* comes
from the Greek adjective *entheos*, which means "God within."[1] An

enthusiastic person does not need to say much, but you know by their expression, their demeanor, and the aura they portray that they are inspired, motivated, and excited about life. Their enthusiasm comes from being full of joy.

Joy is inside of every person who has a re-created spirit. Joy is a characteristic of God. God gave you His life and His nature when He came to make His home in you. One characteristic of God's nature is joy, and that joy lives inside of you!

Happiness and sadness come from the outside in the form of events and circumstances; joy comes from the inside. Happiness occurs when "good" circumstances happen in your life and sadness occurs when "bad" circumstances happen in your life. Adverse circumstances ruin happiness. Joy transcends the emotional roller coaster of circumstance.

2. Is it God's will for you to live a joyful life?

God's Word contains God's will for your life. God's will concerning joy in your life is contained in *God's Master Success Book*.

> By this My Father is glorified, that you bear much
> fruit; so you will be My disciples.
>
> —John 15:8

As a follower of Christ (disciple), your life glorifies God as you bear "much fruit." The fruit Jesus is talking about in this verse is the fruit of your re-created spirit, which includes love, *joy*, peace, patience, kindness, goodness, faithfulness, gentleness, and self-control. God, your heavenly Father, is glorified when you live a joyful life by displaying the fruit of joy.

> God's nature includes joy and it lives inside of you.

> These things I have spoken to you, that My joy
> may remain in you, and that your joy may be full.
>
> —John 15:11

Jesus wants you to have the same joy He has so that your joy will be the fullest possible joy. Your attitude should indicate that you have the joy of Jesus in your life. The joy that created the universe resides in you. That joy is constant, not up and down like happiness and sadness. Living a joyful life means getting off of the emotional roller coaster. You can live an enthusiastic joyful life!

One of the reasons Jesus is so emphatic about you living a joyful life is because He knew that He was going to suffer and pay the price so that you could live a life of victory and triumph. Jesus knew that He was going to make a way for His joy to be available to every person who follows Him. Jesus secured the victory so you could live a joyful life.

> But thanks be to God, Who in Christ always leads us in triumph [as trophies of Christ's victory] and through us spreads and makes evident the fragrance of the knowledge of God everywhere.
> —2 CORINTHIANS 2:14, AMP

As a child of God in Christ, you are a trophy of Christ's victory. You are a trophy of the joy Jesus spoke of in John 15:11. Jesus expects you to display His joy as you confirm His victory. The joy of Jesus is the fragrance that God spreads through you. God is leading you in a triumphant life. No matter

> Jesus loves you so much that His joy is your joy!

what the circumstances are in your life, Jesus made you more than a conqueror so you could en-*joy* life! Jesus loves you so much that His victory is your victory and His joy is your joy.

> Yet amid all these things we are more than conquerors and gain a surpassing victory through Him Who loved us.
> —ROMANS 8:37, AMP

Overwhelming victory is yours. You can live a life of joy, a life that expresses itself with triumphant exuberance. Triumphant exuberance is living a joyful life of victory twenty-four hours a day, seven days a week. God has made you more than a conqueror in this life. You have already gained a surpassing victory over life's trials and tribulations. You can walk in victory and triumph by living a life full of joy. You can live the joyful abundant life that Jesus' sacrifice made available to you. It is God's will for you to live a joyful life!

3. How can you cultivate a joyful life?

Jesus provides you with the key to cultivating a joyful life. Joy develops from a consistent relationship with your heavenly Father through Jesus Christ.

> Until now you have asked nothing in My name. Ask, and you will receive, that your joy may be full.
>
> —John 16:24

You can cultivate a joyful life through prayer. Prayer will help you get off the emotional roller coaster. Prayer is talking to God. Meditating is listening to God. "Asking" refers to speaking to God. "Receiving" refers to hearing from God. According to Jesus, you ask, you receive, and your joy becomes full. It really is that simple. A common mistake is thinking that not asking God for something is a mark of humility. Failure to ask does not show humility; failure to ask shows disobedience to a command from Jesus. You are commanded by Jesus to "ask." Asking and receiving is how you cultivate a joyful life. Answered prayer will cause you to experience the fullest possible joy.

Ask, in Jesus' name, and you will receive, that your joy may be full.

If you do not ask, your joy will not be full. Failing to ask reflects an attitude of pride; it is not a sign of humility. Jesus said that your heavenly Father knows the things you have need of before you ask Him (Matt. 6:8). Then Jesus goes on to say, "Ask, and it will be given to you...for everyone who asks receives" (Matt. 7:7–8).

Asking displays an attitude of humility. Humility is not synonymous with being poor, sick, and defeated. Some sincere religious people think it is a mark of godliness to be poor, sick, and defeated. The Bible repeatedly states the opposite. It is very difficult to have your joy full when you are living in lack and do not have the necessities of life.

God's Master Success Book promises you threefold prosperity (3 John 1:2). First, God wants you to prosper in all of the things you do. Second, God wants you to prosper in your physical body. Third, God wants you to prosper in your soul (in your thoughts and emotions). One of the ways you receive this threefold blessing of prosperity is by asking and receiving. Ask, in Jesus' name, and you will receive, that your joy may be full!

4. How does joy grow in your life?

Joy is one of the fruits of your re-created spirit. You glorify God as the fruit of joy grows in your life. The key to living a life full of joy is habit formation. Everything you do is influenced by your habits. Your habits were formed by repeating the things you do, repeating them over, and over, and over.

There are four steps you can take to form the habit of living a life of joy. Experts say that it takes about thirty days to form a new habit or replace an old habit. You can form or replace habits by following four clearly defined steps. These four steps may require you to take some actions that may be a little uncomfortable for you until you have had some time to

> The key to living a life of joy is habit formation.

practice the steps. The good news is that none of these four steps are difficult. The disciplines necessary to form these new habits are quite simple. The repetition of these disciplines establishes the new habit and makes the new habit permanent.

You can form a healthy new habit of joy during the next thirty days. To form your new habit, practice each of the four steps listed below every day for thirty consecutive days. Your thirty days of action will result in the formation of the habit of living a life filled with joy.

Joy resides in your re-created spirit, and that joy can be manifested in your life as you replace old habits that are holding you back with healthy new habits that establish joy in your life.

As you practice the following four steps you will soon find that you are no longer riding the emotional roller coaster.

Step 1: Make a decision to cultivate joy in your life.

You have a choice to make; the choice to commit yourself to implementing these four steps. You must make the decision to fully commit yourself to forming your healthy productive new habit. The quality decision to fully commit must become a burning desire for you.[2] When you have the burning desire and have committed yourself to action, you are 51 percent of the way to forming your new habit. Making the decision to commit means your emotional roller coaster ride is coming to an end. The establishment of your healthy new habit, joy, will force the emotional roller coaster out of your life. You will no longer experience debilitating lows and deceptive highs. Your establishment of this healthy new habit changes the issue. The issue is not happiness anymore. The issue is no longer a result of circumstances. The issue is your established joy!

> Your attitude is more important than your circumstances.

Step 2: Start speaking joyful words.

Most people equate joy with the absence of adversity and hardship, but joy can be experienced in the midst of adversity and negative circumstances. Your attitude and the words that spring forth from your attitude are far more important than your circumstances.

A man has joy by the answer of his mouth, and a
word spoken in due season, how good it is!
—Proverbs 15:23

Your words should be indicative of the joy you want in your life. As you speak joyful words, your entire attitude toward life will be uplifted. Cultivating joy in your life requires a new attitude. Psalm 118:24 exemplifies this new attitude, "This is the day the Lord has made; let us rejoice and be glad in it" (NIV).

Your attitude should be described as one of rejoicing and being glad. One effective way for you to check your attitude is by listening to yourself answer a very common question, "How are you?" Consider using one of the following words for the next seven days every time someone asks you how you are doing: great, fabulous, excellent, outstanding, terrific, fantastic, or phenomenal. If you will do that for thirty consecutive days you will find the joy in your life has significantly increased. The reason many people respond to "How are you?" in a mediocre manner is because they have formed the habit of answering that way. Start responding with a new positive response, and in about thirty days that positive response will become your habit. Eventually you will find yourself always answering in a joyful manner. Just by responding to "How are you?" with a joyful response will allow you to experience noticeable improvements to the level of joy in your life.

Start speaking good things about yourself. Start talking to yourself in a positive manner. Start saying what God's Word says about you. First thing in the morning when you wake up say audibly and with emphasis something positive about yourself, such as, "I am full of joy today!" "I have the joy of Jesus in me!" "This is going to be a great day!" "I believe God is

> Your words birth the outcomes in your life.

going to do something wonderful in my life today!" Repeat those phrases two or three times, and your day will start in a positive, joyful manner.

You can break the habit of getting your feelings and emotions solely from your circumstances. Sometimes your feelings and emotions are unstable, sometimes they are unreliable, and in some cases they are simply deceptions you have chosen to believe. The feelings and emotions you experience in your life, whether positive or negative, have been produced in your life by the habits you have formed due to the choices you have made. You can continue to create the way you feel by reacting to your circumstances, or you can create the way you feel by responding to your circumstances with positive words. Always remember that your tongue has creative power. You can birth the outcomes in your life with the words that come out of your mouth.

> Death and life are in the power of the tongue, And
> those who love it will eat its fruit.
> —PROVERBS 18:21

The word *fruit* refers to results. The results you are currently experiencing in your life were influenced by the words that came out of your mouth. The word *death* refers to negative results; *life* refers to positive results. The choice is yours. Jesus said that you will have whatever you say (Mark 11:23).

You must be diligent and consistent to form the habit of speaking positive joy-filled words. The joy in your life is influenced by your words. Your circumstances will line up with your thoughts, words, and actions.

Step 3: Control your thought life.

A thought takes place before a word is spoken. You are saying what you say on a regular basis because of what is in your mind. Sometimes your mind can be filled with how bad everything seems. The pressures of society are reflected in the six o'clock and eleven o'clock news. Whatever you fill your mind with is what will eventually become your expression. You are not to dwell on negative influences; you are to restrict negative influences. It becomes increasingly more difficult to speak positive words when your mind is continually subjected to negativity.

Controlling your thought life pleases God. Think thoughts that are found in *God's Master Success Book*. What you think about most becomes your meditation. Meditate on Philippians 4:8 thoughts.

> And now, dear brothers and sisters, one final thing. Fix your thoughts on what is true, and honorable, and right, and pure, and lovely, and admirable. Think about things that are excellent and worthy of praise.
>
> —PHILIPPIANS 4:8, NLT

Philippians 4:8 lists the type of thoughts you are to meditate on. Notice that nowhere does it mention thinking about negative circumstances. God gave you free will, and it is your responsibility to fill your mind with positive thoughts. As you continually think about the success principles found in God's Word, your negative circumstances will start to change.

Your thoughts can cause you to become depressed, dejected, and unhappy. The person who is continually unhappy in life is the person whose mind is continually filled with negative thoughts. It is really up to you whether you are depressed or full of joy.

Everyone is a creature of habit. The way you behave is a result of the conditioning you have received and accepted. Your habits

> It is your responsibility to fill your mind with positive thoughts.

start in your mind and are always a function of your thoughts. You learned to swim, ride a bicycle, and drive a car by consciously doing these things over and over again. These activities and actions became a habit—an automatic action. Every individual is free to choose to develop good habits or bad habits.

If you repeat negative thoughts, words, and actions over a period of time, you will be under the compulsion of the negative habit you have inadvertently formed. The same is true of positive thoughts, words, and actions. Whether positive or negative, whether intentional or inadvertent, you get what you form. When you reprogram your mind by renewing it with the habit of joyful thinking, you will experience joyful living. You will be acting on God's Word, and your circumstances will begin to change because your thoughts, words, and actions agree with God's Word, which is the source of all joy.

Controlling your thought life is a spiritual battle. Your natural thinking mind is continually challenged to maintain God's thoughts. Your thinking will be transformed, and you will experience a joyful life when controlling your thoughts becomes a habit.

Step 4: Live a life of faith.

Living a life of faith pleases God (Heb. 11:6). The challenge to living a life of faith comes when negative circumstances attempt to rob you of your joy. You are admonished to live by faith, and not by the circumstances you can see.

> We live by faith, not by sight.
> —2 CORINTHIANS 5:7, NIV

The word *sight* refers to one of the five physical senses. Govern your life by faith in God's Word and not solely by what you see or how you feel. You can learn how to live a life of faith the same way the apostle Paul learned to live a life of faith.

> **Controlling your thoughts is a spiritual battle.**

> Not that I am implying that I was in any personal want, for I have learned how to be content (satisfied to the point where I am not disturbed or disquieted) in whatever state I am. I know how to be abased and live humbly in straitened circumstances, and I know also how to enjoy plenty and live in abundance. I have learned in any and all circumstances the secret of facing every situation, whether well-fed

or going hungry, having a sufficiency and enough
to spare or going without and being in want. I have
strength for all things in Christ Who empowers
me [I am ready for anything and equal to anything
through Him Who infuses inner strength into me;
I am self-sufficient in Christ's sufficiency].
—PHILIPPIANS 4:11–13, AMP

The apostle Paul learned to be content whatever the circumstances. When you live by faith, you live independent of circumstances. Joy is the result of practicing your faith, the result of putting your faith into action. The faith life is not dictated by circumstances and is not restricted by the five physical senses. Faith not only acts independently of your senses, but faith acts independently of your circumstances. Your joy is not dependent on your circumstances; your joy is dependent on following the instructions in *God's Master Success Book*.

The apostle Paul learned the secret of being content in any and every situation. You can follow Paul's example and learn to be content whatever your current temporary circumstances. Paul's response to adversity was not to become depressed. Paul's response was to claim that he could do all things through Christ who strengthened him. Paul learned how to live in victory whether he was hungry or full, experiencing need or enjoying abundance. Paul knew his sufficiency was found in Christ. Paul's attitude exemplified biblical faith.

Paul knew where his help was coming from. His sufficiency came from his faith in Christ. The reality of the risen Christ was the source of Paul's joy. The source of Paul's ability to retain his joy was his union with Christ. Paul's strength in Christ was the secret that allowed him to be joyful as he went through a variety of very difficult circumstances.

You can adopt the attitude of the apostle Paul. You have free will; you can initiate your own attitude adjustment. The next time trials occur in your life, you can respond with: "I can do all things through Christ who strengthens me." When you make that bold confession, you will be releasing the power of God into your life. God's power manifests when you release your faith by speaking God's Word.

Living by faith is living independently of circumstances. Living by faith is speaking God's Word regardless of how you feel. Rather than relying solely on your feelings and circumstances, follow the example that was provided for you; live by faith!

You have a choice to make. Jesus stated that His joy is your joy. Your joy can be full, complete, and overflowing twenty-four hours a day, seven days a week. In the midst of adverse circumstances, you can react to those circumstances or you can proactively respond by doing what God's Word instructs you to do.

> My brethren, count it all joy when you fall into
> various trials, knowing that the testing of your
> faith produces patience.
>
> —JAMES 1:2–3

Trials are negative circumstances that will inevitably occur in your life. Your reaction to negative circumstances can make you feel defeated and depressed. Your proactive response to negative circumstances can resolve your problems and develop your character. Since you are now a child of God, you now have God's help to turn your negative circumstances into a lesson in developing character. During your Christian walk you will develop character, regardless of whether or not you want to. The only issue is how many times you will repeat the lesson before you learn it and move on.

You can do everything you need to do through Christ who gives you strength.

Some people want to have a pity party when they encounter negative circumstances. The cause of their negative, miserable attitude is their refusal to act on God's Word and count it all joy. Some people consider their feelings and emotions to be more important than what is written in *God's Master Success Book*. Some people insist on acting out however they happen to feel. Stubbornly retaining a bad attitude causes God's power to remain idle in the lives of these people. God responds when His children count it all joy, not when His children bellyache and complain. *God's Master Success Book* instructs you to keep your attitude positive and to be joyful during your trials.

Make a decision to start using your new habit of counting it all joy when you experience trials and negative circumstances. Many people have been conditioned to react negatively to negative circumstances. When you continue to react to negative circumstances with any attitude other than joy, you keep getting more of those negative circumstances.

Faith and fear both expect something to happen that has not yet happened. Faith produces positive results; fear produces negative results. Fear is negative faith. You will experience negative circumstances in your life if you activate fear by speaking negative words. Release your faith by speaking joyful words in the face of your negative circumstances and you

> Times of trials are times of growth.

will see God's power manifested in your life. When you act on God's Word in the face of negative circumstances, you are responding in faith and your circumstances will start to improve.

You are either forming positive or negative habits depending on your thoughts, words, and actions. The process of forming habits is producing the results in your life. What you allow to occupy your mind will sooner or later determine your speech and your actions.

The Book of Acts records an account of severely negative circumstances and the impressive success that resulted from maintaining joy. (See Acts 16:1–34.) The apostle Paul and his ministry partner, Silas, were on a missionary trip in the Roman colony of Philippi when they encountered a girl who had a demon spirit through which she predicted the future. The girl followed Paul and Silas for many days and mocked God right in front of them. Paul became annoyed and ordered the demon spirit out of her. This cut into the livelihood of the people who were making money from the girl's fortune-telling ability. Those who profited from the girl's fortune-telling seized Paul and Silas, brought them before the city officials, and accused them of violating Roman customs.

> Then the multitude rose up together against them; and the magistrates tore off their clothes and commanded them to be beaten with rods. And when they had laid many stripes on them, they threw them into prison, commanding the jailer to keep them securely. Having received such a charge, he put them into the inner prison and fastened their feet in the stocks.
>
> —Acts 16:22–24

Paul and Silas were beaten and thrown into jail. Instead of complaining and bellyaching, Paul and Silas exhibited their inner joy by praying and singing hymns to God in the midst of their adversity. As Paul and Silas prayed and sang, God's power manifested supernaturally in their situation.

> But at midnight Paul and Silas were praying and singing hymns to God, and the prisoners were listening to them. Suddenly there was a great earthquake, so that the foundations of the prison were shaken; and immediately all the doors were opened and everyone's chains were loosed.
>
> —Acts 16:25–26

Not only were Paul and Silas soon released from prison, but they were also successful in their ministry. Even the jailer and his family soon accepted Christ as their Savior and were baptized. Paul and Silas were called to spread the gospel of Jesus Christ, and they accomplished their purpose in the midst of exceedingly negative circumstances. Paul and Silas did not react to the pain and discomfort dictated by their senses, but instead they responded to the Word of God. God's power will be displayed in your life just as miraculously as it did in the lives of Paul and Silas when you act on God's Word just as Paul and Silas did.

Your joy thermostat is set by the way you are thinking, what you are saying, and how you are acting. The instructions for obtaining joy in your life are found in *God's Master Success Book*. You can increase the amount of joy in your life by spending more time with God and more time meditating on God's Word. As you continually think, speak, and act according to the principles in *God's Master Success Book*, your joy will soar. You can change the way you feel by changing the way you think, changing what you say, and changing how you act.

> You can change the way you feel by changing the way you think, changing what you say, and changing how you act.

CHAPTER PRINCIPLES

1. Happiness is a state of mind, but joy is a state of being.

2. Joy is not dependent on circumstances. Joy is based on knowing who you are in Christ.

3. Joy is a characteristic of the nature of God within you.

4. Your attitude should indicate that you have the joy of Jesus in your life.

5. You can walk in victory and triumph by living a life full of joy.

6. You can cultivate a joyful life through prayer.

7. Ask, in Jesus' name, and you will receive, that your joy may be full.

8. Habit formation is the key to living a life full of joy. Your habits are producing the results in your life.

9. Your attitude is more important than your circumstances.

10. Your tongue has creative power. Speak joyful words.

11. Your words should be indicative of the joy you want in your life.

12. God's power manifests when you release your faith by speaking God's Word.

13. It is your responsibility to fill your mind with positive thoughts.

14. Controlling your thought life is a spiritual battle.

15. You can do everything you need to do through Christ who gives you strength.

16. Your times of trials are times of growth.

17. You will develop character as you learn from your mistakes.

18. You increase the amount of joy in your life as you spend more time with God and His Word.

19. You change the way you feel by changing the way you think, changing what you speak, and changing how you act.

20. It is God's will for you to live a joyful life!

Chapter 9

KEYS TO SETTING AND ACHIEVING YOUR GOALS

SETTING AND ACHIEVING goals are the intermediate steps on the way to realizing your God-given dream. The process of setting and achieving goals is an integral part of realizing your God-given dream. Setting and achieving goals are steps that help you to complete the work that has been assigned to you.

Goal setting requires faith. Setting goals and making plans for their attainment helps you to be sure of what you hope for and certain of what you do not see (Heb. 11:1, NIV). You are asking for God's assistance when you set goals and make plans for their attainment. Goal setting is a proactive process that helps you become a better receiver.

The biblical account of an Old Testament prophet named Habakkuk provides insight into setting and achieving goals. Habakkuk lived around 600 B.C. at the time when Babylon was becoming the dominant world power and Judah would soon feel Babylon's destructive force. Habakkuk was made to understand that God was going to use the Babylonians to judge the people of Judah. Habakkuk also knew that the Babylonians were wicked and the people of Judah considered themselves to be righteous. Habakkuk had difficulty understanding why God was going to use the wicked to judge those who were relatively righteous.

The Old Testament Book of Habakkuk is a conversation between Habakkuk and God. It is a series of the Old Testament prophet's questions and God's answers to those questions. Habakkuk's questions included: "Why do the wicked seem to be winning?" "Why isn't God doing something about all the problems in the world?" "Why is there so much injustice?" Habakkuk's questions are timeless; they are questions that occur to everyone. The answers God gave to Habakkuk are as valid and relevant today as they were when God gave them to Habakkuk.

Habakkuk's questions were really Habakkuk's questionings of God, not his questions to God. Habakkuk's questions were really a disguise for complaining. Habakkuk was perplexed that wickedness, strife, and oppression were rampant in Judah but God seemingly did nothing. When told that the Lord was preparing to do something about it through the ruthless Babylonians, Habakkuk's perplexity only intensified. How could a just God use the wicked Babylonians to punish a people more righteous than themselves? God's answers to Habakkuk's questionings provide the keys to setting and achieving goals.

After Habakkuk had stated his second complaint, he went to the watchtower to wait for God's reply. Habakkuk wanted to be in the best position to receive God's message.

> I will climb up to my watchtower and stand at my
> guardpost. There I will wait to see what the LORD
> says and how he will answer my complaint.
> —HABAKKUK 2:1, NLT

Habakkuk assumed a cautious posture as He waited to hear God's reply. Old Testament prophets often used the watchtower as a symbol representing an attitude of expectation. Habakkuk was prepared to hear God's answer and receive God's revelation.

WRITE THE VISION

God's response to Habakkuk's complaint opens with a command. God's command provides the first key to effectively setting and achieving goals. God told Habakkuk to write down his vision.

> And the Lord answered me and said, Write the vision and engrave it so plainly upon tablets that everyone who passes may [be able to] read [it easily and quickly] as he hastens by.
> —HABAKKUK 2:2, AMP

The vision contained severe punishments for Babylonian atrocities committed against neighboring countries. The various steps to the end of the cruelty of Babylonian domination were "goals" that Habakkuk wanted to be attained; "goals" that God stated would be attained. Habakkuk obeyed God's command and acted on God's instructions by writing down the steps necessary to achieve his vision. When you write down the steps (goals) necessary to achieve your vision (God-given dream), you are obeying God and acting on His instructions.

The first key to effectively setting and achieving goals is to write them down. God has His goals written down. The Bible contains God's written plan and vision for the universe and for mankind. Some topics included in God's written plan: how and why God created the earth, why mankind is here, how life works, what things to avoid, and what to expect in the future.

> The first step to achieving your goals is to write them down.

Goals must be identified to be achieved. Writing your goals forces you to decide what you want out of life. Effective goal setting requires that you identify three things: what you want to be, what you want to do, and what you want to have. "To be" goals include improving yourself through the books you read, the CDs you listen to, and the people you associate with. "To do" goals involve activities and events that provide satisfaction and productivity. Examples of "to do" goals include performing a certain job, getting elected to a community service organization, teaching less fortunate children, or climbing a mountain. "To have" goals involve the material aspects of life, such as money and possessions.

God can do exceedingly abundantly above all that you ask or think (Eph. 3:20). However, if you do not know where you want to go, you will be unable to identify your specific goal. You must clearly identify your goal to receive God's assistance in achieving that goal.

Write down the goals that are necessary to make your vision your reality. When you write down your goals, you then know where you are going. God begins to move on your behalf when you know the direction you want for your life. God will give you the assistance you need to achieve your goals. He will cause people, events, and material assistance to come into your life.[1]

> Writing your goals inspires you to take action on the ideas God reveals to you.

Writing your goals inspires you to take action on the ideas God reveals to you. Take at least one action step every day in each of your three goal areas: to be, to do, and to have. If your goal is to write a book, write something every day, even if it is just one paragraph. If your goal is improved physical fitness, do some type of exercise every day, even if it is just a short walk. If your goal is to move into a nicer home, set aside some money every day, even if it is just one dollar.

You are instructed in *God's Master Success Book* to write your goals down for three very significant reasons. First, to decide what kind of life you want; second, so God can move on your behalf; and third, so you can take focused action toward the accomplishment of your specific goals.

WAIT EXPECTANTLY

Habakkuk's second complaint contains a complaint within a complaint. Habakkuk's second complaint is concerned with how a just God could use such very wicked people to punish Judah. During the second complaint Habakkuk interjects an additional complaint by pointing out to God that it is He who has allowed, and even continues in the future to allow, the wickedness of the Babylonians to go unpunished. God's response is to assure Habakkuk that Babylon will be punished and faith will be rewarded; that events will happen at the time He has appointed.

> This vision is for a future time. It describes the end,
> and it will be fulfilled. If it seems slow in coming,
> wait patiently, for it will surely take place. It will
> not be delayed.
> —HABAKKUK 2:3, NLT

The phrase "If it seems slow in coming, wait patiently" does not mean that you are to sit around and do nothing. You are to act on the instructions in *God's Master Success Book*. You are to exercise patience until your goal is attained. You are to exercise biblical patience, and biblical patience is waiting without complaining.

Your God-given dream is for an appointed time. The appointed time is set for God's timing. God chose when you were to be born for a reason. You were born at the right time to realize your God-given dream. This is your time!

Your vision will come to pass, but in the meantime, review your vision (God-given dream) and take action on your goals. Walking by faith will encourage you to persevere and persist during your time of waiting. Faith is released through words; speak your goals into existence! Your God-given dream will come to pass at exactly the right time.

> God's timing occurs when you have prepared yourself.

123

> Look at the proud! They trust in themselves and
> their lives are crooked.
>
> —Habakkuk 2:4, nlt

One of the challenges of waiting is the temptation to rely on yourself to expedite results without embracing God's timing. God is the one who is able to bring your vision to pass. You, like Habakkuk, are to wait expectantly for God's timing. You are to be confident that God is producing the results in your life according to the thoughts you think and the words you speak. God's timing will occur when you have prepared yourself. When you are ready, you will accomplish your goals.

Live by Faith

God told Habakkuk to wait patiently and live by faith. Habakkuk's faith gave him the confidence to share his vision with the people of his day. Habakkuk's faith gave Judah hope for the future and continues to provide a basis for hope even today. Just like Habakkuk, you need to live by faith. Living by faith will empower you to achieve the goals that God has enabled you to accomplish.

> Living by faith will empower you to achieve the goals that God has enabled you to accomplish.

> But the just shall live by his faith.
>
> —Habakkuk 2:4

The phrase "the just shall live by faith" is repeated three times in the New Testament and all three references are found in the Epistles, the instructional letters written to be shared by all the churches over time. (See Romans 1:17; Galatians 3:11; Hebrews 10:38.) God justified you (made you righteous) and now you are expected to live by faith.

The power you need to accomplish your goals and realize your

God-given dream is released through faith. Faith is the substance of things hoped for and the evidence of things not seen. Faith gives substance to the goals you want to achieve. Faith is the thought-image of your goals already completed. The only evidence you need is the picture you hold in your mind of you in possession of your goals. The world calls it visualization or positive thinking; however, the techniques of visualization and positive thinking are simply applied faith. Applied faith is the belief that the images you picture in your mind will become real. Imagine your goals as already accomplished.

The story of James Nesmeth illustrates the power of picturing images in your mind. Major James Nesmeth, an average weekend golfer shooting in the mid-to-low nineties, dreamed of improving his golf game. But, then, for seven years he never touched a club nor set foot on a fairway. During those years, however, he developed an amazingly effective technique for improving his game. The first time he returned to a course, he shot an astonishing seventy-four! He had cut twenty strokes off his average. What was his secret? Visualization. For those seven years, Major Nesmeth was a prisoner of war in North Vietnam. He was imprisoned in a cage four and one-half feet high and five feet long. Most of those years, he saw no one, talked to no one, and had no

> Empower your God-given dream; visualize it!

physical activity. He knew he had to find some way to occupy his mind or he would lose his sanity, so he began to visualize playing golf. Each day, he played a full eighteen holes at the imaginary country club of his dreams. He imagined every detail, every shot. And not once did he miss a shot or putt. Seven days a week, four hours a day, he played eighteen holes in his mind.[2]

Your God-given dream requires your assistance to become your reality. Put your faith into action; visualize your goals and imagine reaching them. See yourself setting and achieving all of your goals. Create in your mind an image of you already living your God-given dream.

You are to write down your goals and wait expectantly as God provides opportunities for you to accomplish your goals. You are to live by faith, knowing that your God-given dream will surely come to pass. When negative circumstances bring your plans to a halt, it is not enough to just keep going and not give up. You must respond to the lack of visible results the way Habakkuk did.

Praise and Thank God

Habakkuk did something in the face of negative circumstances. Habakkuk's action reveals the appropriate response to negative circumstances. God told Habakkuk to write down his vision. God told Habakkuk to be patient as God would cause Habakkuk's vision to come to pass. God told Habakkuk to live by faith. Habakkuk took significant action when confronted by negative circumstances. Habakkuk's action-response contains your answer to negative circumstances and negative events.

> Even though the fig trees have no blossoms, and there are no grapes on the vines; even though the olive crop fails, and the fields lie empty and barren; even though the flocks die in the fields, and the cattle barns are empty.
> —Habakkuk 3:17, nlt

With the farm crops failed and the farm animals dead, the situation looks bleak for Habakkuk and his people. With famine in the land and the world-renowned cruelty of the Babylonians on the horizon, Habakkuk and his people would encounter dismal circumstances and a lack of visible results. Habakkuk's response to these discouraging circumstances should also be your response to discouraging circumstances. Habakkuk's response to dismal circumstances is your answer to preventing discouragement and frustration while enabling the power of God.

> Yet I will rejoice in the LORD! I will be joyful in
> the God of my salvation!
> —HABAKKUK 3:18, NLT

Habakkuk's action-response was to rejoice in the Lord! The third chapter in the Book of Habakkuk is a prayer, which Habakkuk sang. Habakkuk's response to the most dismal of circumstances was to sing and praise God.[3] The Old Testament prophet, Habakkuk, had learned to have joy in his life regardless of circumstances. Habakkuk had a source of strength that sustained him during dismal circumstances.

> The Sovereign LORD is my strength!
> —HABAKKUK 3:19, NLT

Habakkuk knew where his strength for the victory would come from. The Lord God was his strength. Habakkuk's prayer praises God for who He is, what He has done, and what He is going to do. Habakkuk thanked God in advance for the accomplishment of his vision.

Habakkuk had learned to live by faith and to trust in God's providence regardless of circumstances. Habakkuk's response to suffering and loss was to praise and thank God. When negative circumstances come into your life, praise and thank God for who He is, what He has done, and what He is going to do.

When you encounter opposition to your goals, praise the Lord and remain joyful. Through all of the trials during your life, maintain an attitude of praise and thanksgiving to God. That is what Habakkuk did and you can do it too!

Praising God, while maintaining a joyful attitude, is an integral part of achieving your goals and realizing your God-given dream.

1. Setting and achieving goals are the intermediate steps on the way to realizing your God-given dream.

2. You are asking for God's assistance when you set goals and make plans for their attainment.

3. The first step to achieving your goals is to write them down.

4. Writing your goals forces you to decide what you want. Effective goal setting requires that you identify three things: what you want to be, what you want to do, and what you want to have.

5. Writing your goals inspires you to take action on the ideas God reveals to you.

6. You are to exercise patience, perseverance, and persistence until your goals are attained.

7. You were born at the right time to realize your God-given dream.

8. Faith is released through words; speak your goals into existence!

9. God's timing will occur when you have prepared yourself.

10. Living by faith will empower you to achieve the goals that God has enabled you to accomplish.

11. Put your faith into action; visualize your goals and imagine reaching them.

12. Thank God in advance for the realization of your God-given dream.

13. When negative circumstances come into your life, praise and thank God for who He is, what He has done, and what He is going to do.

14. Through all of the trials during your life, maintain an attitude of praise and thanksgiving to God.

Chapter 10

The Power Within You

E PHESIANS 3:20 MAKES one of the most remarkable statements in all of God's Word. Ephesians 3:20 sums up what is available to the believer who takes action on the principles contained in *God's Master Success Book*.

> Now to him who is able to do immeasurably more
> than all we ask or imagine, according to his power
> that is at work within us.
> —EPHESIANS 3:20, NIV

This verse explains the power that resides within you and what that power makes available to you. Meditate on Ephesians 3:20 one phrase at a time:

1. Now to Him who is able to do
2. Immeasurably more
3. Than all we ask or imagine
4. According to His power that is at work within us

1. Now to Him who is able to do

God is the One who is able to do great and mighty things in your life. You have available to you the rights and privileges that are extended to a child of God. Your rights and privileges were bought at a very high price, paid for by the ultimate sacrifice. God has taken great care to make His protection and provision available to you. To tap into the force that created the universe, it is necessary to acknowledge the One who is able to do great and mighty things in your life.

God deserves your worship, your praise, and your thanks because of who He is, the love that He has for you, and the provisions He has made for you. Worship God because of everything He is. Praise God for everything He has done, everything He is doing, and everything He will continue to do during your life. Give God thanks that you are a child of God, a member of God's royal family. Worship, praise, and thanksgiving open the door to the blessings of God.

> Worship, praise, and thanksgiving open the door to the blessings of God.

2. Immeasurably more

God is able to do immeasurably more than you ask or imagine. He can do the miraculous in your life. You are never alone. God is with you. Your situation is never impossible; God is in you and for you.

There is more to your life than what you are currently seeing and experiencing. God is always doing something in your life that you cannot see. God is able to do immeasurably more in your life because of His unlimited power. As you learn to live by faith and walk in love, God's unlimited power is released into your life.

3. Than all we ask or imagine

God is able to do immeasurably more than all you ask or imagine. You cannot ask anything or imagine anything that is beyond

God's power. You are the one who is to do the asking and you are the one who is to do the imagining. God is the One who is able to do immeasurably more than all you ask or imagine.

You empower what you ask for by speaking words. Speak complaints and grumblings, and you have influenced your future. Speak praise and thanksgiving, and you have influenced your future. Your results reflect your attitude. Your attitude is influenced by the words you speak and the thoughts you imagine.

To imagine goes beyond merely thinking thoughts. Effective imagining includes forming a mental image of the realization of your God-given dream. Your future reality will be determined in part by what you imagine today. Your imagination enables you to see something in the spiritual realm before it is manifested in the physical realm. See yourself living your God-given dream!

> Your attitude is influenced by the words you speak and the thoughts you imagine.

God speaks of nonexistent things as if they already existed (Rom. 4:17). God created the physical universe by calling it into existence. He created what is visible from what cannot be seen (Heb. 11:3). You were created in God's image and you can follow God's example by using your words and your imagination to move toward your God-given dream. Speak your God-given dream and imagine living your God-given dream.

4. According to His power that is at work within us

The power that is at work within you is the indwelling presence of the Holy Spirit. The Spirit of God, the Holy Spirit, resides within you. Your body is the temple of God, His dwelling place.

> Do you not know that you are the temple of God
> and that the Spirit of God dwells in you?
> —1 CORINTHIANS 3:16

131

> Or do you not know that your body is the temple
> of the Holy Spirit who is in you, whom you have
> from God, and you are not your own?
>
> —1 Corinthians 6:19

Your body is the temple of the Holy Spirit. Under the old covenant, God's presence was confined to the temple building. Under the new covenant, your body is the temple within which the Holy Spirit dwells. The presence and power of God now reside within you in the person of the Holy Spirit. You can be confident that the power of God is going to work effectively in your life because of the indwelling presence of the Holy Spirit.

You should be ever conscious that the Holy Spirit resides within you. You may hear other men and women complain about their lack of power, their lack of ability, and all that they cannot do. However, you now know that the God of all possibility resides within you. You are not permitted to join others, Christian or otherwise, in a boring pity party.

God's power dwells within every believer. Jesus stated that all things are possible to the person who believes (Mark 9:23). Jesus knew that when He returned to heaven, the God of all possibility would come to dwell within every believer. The Holy Spirit is both your ability and your strength. He will enable you and empower you in all you do.

> The Holy Spirit resides within you; the power of God will work effectively through you.

You cannot have a lack of ability because the Creator of the universe shares His ability with you. You cannot have a lack of strength because the Creator of the universe shares His strength with you. You have the ability and you have the strength because the power of God in person of the Holy Spirit resides within you.

Supernatural power is available to you for the accomplishment of your goals and the realization of your God-given dream because of the indwelling presence of the Holy Spirit. The Holy Spirit will help you establish your success.

> But you shall receive power (ability, efficiency, and
> might) when the Holy Spirit has come upon you.
> —Acts 1:8, amp

The power you need, the ability you need, the wisdom you need, and the strength you need to be a success in life were imparted to you when you received the gift of the Holy Spirit. The plans, the necessary steps, and the details for the accomplishment of your goals and the realization of your God-given dream will be revealed to you during your times of daily fellowship with the Holy Spirit.

> The Holy Spirit will enable you and empower you in all you do.

> However, I am telling you nothing but the truth
> when I say it is profitable (good, expedient, advan-
> tageous) for you that I go away. Because if I do
> not go away, the Comforter (Counselor, Helper,
> Advocate, Intercessor, Strengthener, Standby) will
> not come to you [into close fellowship with you];
> but if I go away, I will send Him to you [to be in
> close fellowship with you].
> —John 16:7, amp

Jesus said that the Holy Spirit would be your Comforter, Counselor, Helper, Advocate, Intercessor, Strengthener, and Standby.

> If you need peace, He is your Comforter.
> If you need wisdom, He is your Counselor.
> If you need assistance, He is your Helper.
> If you need counsel, He is your Advocate.
> If you need prayer, He is your Intercessor.

If you need strength, He is your Strengthener.
If you need fellowship, He is your Standby.

The presence of the Holy Spirit living in you will do everything that Jesus said He would do for you. You always have the Holy Spirit within you to assist you in every area of your life.[1]

Christians who talk of their lack and inability are failing to exercise their rights and privileges as children of God. It is your responsibility to make the effort to learn your rights and privileges. As you spend time in fellowship with the Holy Spirit, He will help you apply your rights and privileges to your life.

> You, dear children, are from God and have overcome them, because the one who is in you is greater than the one who is in the world.
>
> —1 John 4:4, niv

The greater One with His great ability is living within you. Nothing that you encounter or experience in this world is greater than the Holy Spirit. There is no situation or condition that must remain unfavorable. You can face life's challenges with the attitude of a conqueror because He who is in you is greater than he who is in the world. You are a conqueror and much more in this life because of the indwelling presence and power of the Holy Spirit.

> Yet amid all these things we are more than conquerors and gain a surpassing victory through Him Who loved us.
>
> —Romans 8:37, amp

To be effective as a conqueror in this life, you must learn how to let the Holy Spirit be productive in your life. You must learn how to release the power, ability, wisdom, and strength that reside within you. You become effective when you allow the Holy Spirit to empower you by applying the following principles from *God's Master Success Book*:

1. Do not speak negative things about yourself. Do not say you cannot when God has made it clear that you can.

2. Give thanks to God because you are His child and a member of His royal family.

3. Make a daily confession of who you are, what you have, and what you can do because you are in Christ.

4. Act like the "more than a conqueror" that you are.

5. Discuss your goals and how you can achieve them during your fellowship time with the Holy Spirit.

6. Imagine yourself living your God-given dream.

7. Use your words to move toward your God-given dream.

Practicing these seven principles will help you rapidly move toward the achievement of your goals. The indwelling presence of the Holy Spirit will guide you as you move toward the realization of your God-given dream.

God is able to do immeasurably more than all you ask or imagine according to His power that is at work within you. The Holy Spirit will lead you, guide you, motivate you, and inspire you toward the realization of your God-given dream. God's power becomes effective in your life as you cooperate with the Holy Spirit.

> God's power becomes effective in your life as you cooperate with the Holy Spirit.

CHAPTER PRINCIPLES

1. God is the One who is able to do great and mighty things in your life.

2. God's protection and provision belong to you.

3. Worship, praise, and thanksgiving open the door to the blessings of God.

4. God is able to do immeasurably more than all you ask or imagine.

5. Your attitude is influenced by the words you speak and the thoughts you imagine.

6. The power of God will work effectively in your life because of the indwelling presence of the Holy Spirit.

7. You have the ability and strength of God because the presence and power of the Holy Spirit reside within you.

8. The plans, the necessary steps, and the details for the accomplishment of your goals and the realization of your God-given dream will be revealed to you during your times of daily fellowship with the Holy Spirit.

9. Do not speak negative things about yourself. Do not say you cannot when God has made it clear that you can.

10. Give thanks to God because you are His child and a member of His royal family.

11. Make a daily confession of who you are, what you have, and what you can do because you are in Christ.

12. Act like the "more than a conqueror" that you really are.

13. Imagine yourself living your God-given dream.

14. Use your words to move toward your God-given dream.

15. God's power becomes effective in your life as you cooperate with the Holy Spirit.

CONCLUSION

YOU HAVE GOD's wisdom and God's ability at your disposal. You are a limitless individual. There is nothing impossible for you in your life. You are in Christ!

The wisdom of the Creator of the universe is at your disposal. Imagine knowing everything you need to know to be successful in life. That knowledge is available to you through the study of God's Word. Knowledge is what allows you to activate the ability of God that lies dormant within you. Wisdom is what allows you to apply that knowledge at the proper time.

The same mighty power, the same limitless ability that created the universe resides within you. The challenge is for you to release that power and ability for your benefit and for the benefit of others. Wisdom from God will show you how.

Allow the Holy Spirit to let the power of God loose in your life. Allow the Holy Spirit to speak to you through God's Word. Your confidence in God's plan for your life will grow as you meditate on God's Word. *God's Master Success Book* clearly tells you who you are, what you have, and what you can do because you are in Christ. It is now your time to create the abundant life that God has prepared for you.

During your times of daily fellowship, the Holy Spirit will reveal to you the master plan God has for your life. The Holy Spirit will show you the dream God has given to you. The Holy Spirit is your Helper on the journey toward the realization of your God-given dream.

The God in you is the same God who created the entire universe (Col. 1:16). The God in you is the same God who walked across the Sea of Galilee (Mark 6:48–49). The God in you is the same God who took five loaves and two fish and fed more than five thousand people (Matt. 14:21). The God in you is the same God who spoke to the wind and waves and said, "Peace, be still!" (Mark 4:39). The God in you is the same God who raised Lazarus from the dead by speaking the words, "Lazarus, come forth!" (John 11:43). The God in you is the same God who raised Jesus from the dead and seated Him at His own right hand (Eph. 1:20).

God's will is contained in His Word. When your thoughts become agreeable to His will, your plans will be established and successful. God will do His part, but you must do your part. Think, speak, and act according to the principles in *God's Master Success Book*.

There is an unseen realm that is just as real as the world you contact with your five physical senses. What you create in the unseen realm with your thoughts, words, and actions will manifest itself in the realm that you do see, life on earth. You may not always see the outcomes of your thoughts, words, and actions immediately; however, God will always do His part. God is always doing something in your life that you cannot see. Your part is to live by faith and walk in love as you implement the plan for the realization of your God-given dream.

God's life, nature, and ability within you enable and empower you to tap into the force that created the universe. Nothing is impossible for you!

Appendix

Receiving the Presence and Power of God

Y OU CAN HAVE the presence and power of God in your life! Have you passed from spiritual death into spiritual life? Do you know God as your Father? Is His Spirit within your spirit bearing witness that you are a child of God? Do you have the life and nature of God within you?

> If you confess with your mouth that Jesus is Lord and believe in your heart that God raised him from the dead, you will be saved. For it is by believing in your heart that you are made right with God, and it is by confessing with your mouth that you are saved.
> —ROMANS 10:9–10, NLT

Your time to receive eternal life is now. Say the following prayer out loud:

> *Father, I accept Jesus as my Lord. I believe in my heart that You raised Him from the dead so I could be right with You and accepted into Your family. I have eternal life. I have Your life and Your nature within me. I am now saved. Amen.*

God has become your Father and you have become His child; you have been born again. You now have the presence of God within you. Your re-created human spirit is now the home of the Holy Spirit and the Holy Spirit confirms that you are a member of God's family.

> The Spirit Himself bears witness with our spirit that we are children of God.
> —ROMANS 8:16

You have the life and nature of God within you, but you still need the ability of God in order to realize your God-given dream. Being filled with the Holy Spirit enables and empowers you to realize your God-given dream.

> But you shall receive power (ability, efficiency, and might) when the Holy Spirit has come upon you, and you shall be My witnesses in Jerusalem and all Judea and Samaria and to the ends (the very bounds) of the earth.
> —ACTS 1:8, AMP

Your time to be filled with the Holy Spirit is now. Ask, out loud, to be filled with the Holy Spirit:

> *Father, in the name of Jesus, I ask You to fill me with the Holy Spirit. Your ability is now within me. Thank You for Your presence and power. Amen!*

The power of God is now available to you both for your own benefit and for the benefit of others. The Holy Spirit is the power that enables you to share Christ with others. You have God's presence and God's power to assist you as you realize your God-given dream. The limitless ability of the Creator of the universe lies within you just waiting for you to act.

NOTES

INTRODUCTION

1. Josh D. McDowell, *The New Evidence that Demands a Verdict* (Nashville: Thomas Nelson Publishers, 1999), 34.

2. Ibid., 34.

3. Ibid., 37.

4. Ibid., 34.

5. Ibid., 35.

1—THE POWER TWINS

1. At the time Paul wrote this, some early Jewish converts to Christianity thought that Gentiles who were converting to Christianity needed to be circumcised because the Jews were circumcised. Here Paul is stating that circumcision, although part of Jewish customs, was not necessary for those such as the Gentiles who were converting to Christianity. Paul states that which is important is faith working through love.

2. To learn more about living by the principle of faith working through love, order the CD series *Faith Works through Love* from www.beyondpositivethinking.org.

3. The Greek language has different words for different types of love. The books of the New Testament were written almost entirely in Greek, the international language of the time.

2—YOU AND THE FORCE THAT CREATED THE UNIVERSE

1. *Abba* is an Aramaic term for "father."

2. Adam was present watching as Eve disobeyed God's command. God had not put Eve in charge; God had put Adam in

charge. Adam watched Eve disobey, ignored his responsibility, and failed to exercise his authority. Adam had the authority because it was he, not Eve, whom God had previously appointed to have that authority.

3. A listing of the "in Him" scriptures is available at www.beyondpositivethinking.org.

4. Some of the Epistles were addressed to individuals. All of the Epistles were copied and widely circulated among the church as a whole. All of the Epistles were also accepted as being for the benefit of the church as a whole.

5. If you are not yet born again and filled with the Holy Spirit, go to the appendix.

3—RECEIVING YOUR HEART'S DESIRE

1. For a more in depth teaching on realizing your God-given dream and receiving your heart's desire, order the CD series *Realizing Your God-given Dream* from www.beyondpositive-thinking.org.

2. *Vine's Complete Expository Dictionary of Old and New Testament Words* (Nashville: Thomas Nelson, 1984, 1996), s.v. "zoe."

3. The following scriptures state that Jesus is seated at the right hand of God: Matthew 26:64; Mark 14:62; 16:19; Luke 22:69; Acts 2:33–34; Romans 8:34; Ephesians 1:20; Colossians 3:1; Hebrews 1:3; 8:1; 10:12; 12:2; 1 Peter 3:22.

4. To gain a better understanding of the present day ministry of Jesus Christ, order the CD series *The Present Day Ministry of Jesus Christ* from www.beyondpositivethinking.org.

4—Your Thoughts Run Your Life

1. Obviously we cannot know all of God's thoughts or everything that God thinks. However, we can embrace God's thoughts that are available to us through His Word, the Holy Bible.

2. For a more in depth teaching on living out of your recreated spirit, order the CD series *Living Out of Your Re-Created Spirit* from www.beyondpositivethinking.org.

5—Living on God's Frequency

1. *Vine's Complete Expository Dictionary*, s.vv. "phileo," "agape."

2. "Love your neighbor as yourself" is stated eight times in the Bible: Leviticus 19:18; Matthew 19:19; Matthew 22:39; Mark 12:31; Luke 10:27; Romans 13:9; Galatians 5:14; James 2:8.

3. The majority of the love scriptures are located in 1 Corinthians 13 and in the Book of 1 John.

4. A CD of the Love scriptures is available at www.beyond-positivethinking.org.

6—How to be Successful in Life

1. "Press on. Nothing in the world can take the place of persistence. Talent will not; nothing is more common than unsuccessful men with talent. Genius will not; unrewarded genius is almost a proverb. Education will not; the world is full of educated derelicts. Persistence and determination alone are omnipotent." Quote by Calvin Coolidge found at http://find-quotations.com/quote/by/Calvin_Coolidge (accessed October 2, 2010).

2. To some people, success means the gaining of wealth. However, financial success does not necessarily lead to fulfill-

ment. Many people who win the lottery are worse off after they get the money than they were before they had the money. The reason for this enigma is because they have not become the kind of person who is prepared to receive a large sum of money. If you want to make a million dollars, become a million-dollar person!

3. Joshua, the writer of the sixth book of the Bible, did not have the entire Old Testament available to him. Joshua had the wisdom of Moses, which included the Ten Commandments and the moral and ceremonial laws found in the Pentateuch, the first five books of the Bible.

4. Writing God's success principles on index cards will help you internalize the principles. Place each index card where you will see it during the day. When you see the card, speak the success principle on the card.

5. Your reference group, the people you spend time with, will be one of the most influential factors in determining your success in life. Charlie "Tremendous" Jones said that the person you will be in five years will be determined by the books you read and the people you associate with. You choose what you read and who you spend your time with. God created you to have fellowship with Him through the process of realizing your God-given dream. Make God the center of your reference group! Charlie Jones quote found at http://kirkweisler.com/t4d/2008/02/19/charlie-tremendous-jones/ (accessed October 2, 2010).

6. Simon (Peter), James, John, Andrew, and Philip were all fishermen by trade.

7. *Disciple* means follower of Christ, not solely an apostle.

7—Programming Your Success Mechanism

1. Some of the more influential books on success include: *As a Man Thinketh* by James Allen, *Think and Grow Rich* by Napoleon Hill, *The Power of Your Subconscious Mind* by Joseph Murphy, *The Magic of Thinking Big* by David J. Schwartz, *The Magic of Believing* by Claude M. Bristol, and *Psycho-Cybernetics* by Maxwell Maltz. These are all good books and every student of success would benefit from reading them.

2. A controversy exists between those who view man as having two parts; material and immaterial (dichotomy), and those who view man as having three parts; spirit, soul, and body (trichotomy). The issue is whether the immaterial aspects, spirit and soul, are separate divisable parts or portions of one eternal inseparable whole. In either case the characteristics of immaterial versus the characteristics of the spirit and the soul are essentially the same. Whether or not the spirit and the soul are separate parts or two portions of one inseparable whole does not change the way the success mechanism works. Since the functions and characteristics of the spirit and the soul are distinguishable from each other, spirit and soul have been defined in terms of functions and characteristics to enable the reader to easily identify specific functions and characteristics that are relevant to the success mechanism.

3. *Vine's Complete Expository Dictionary*, s.v. "spirit."

4. Ibid., s.v. "soul."

5. Ibid., s.v. "heart."

6. Parables consisted of stories out of everyday life that Jesus used to illustrate spiritual or moral truth, sometimes in the form of brief similes, comparisons, analogies, or proverbial sayings.

7. Statistics from Earl Nightingale, *Lead the Field* (Niles, IL: Nightingale-Conant, 1990).

8. For more on the subject of faith and money, order the CD

series *Passing the Money Test* from www.beyondpositivethinking. org.

8—The Emotional Roller Coaster

1. The source of the word *enthusiasm* is the Greek *enthousias-mos*, which ultimately comes from the adjective *entheos*, "having the god within," formed from *en*, "in, within," and *theos*, "god." Information found at http://www.answers.com/topic/enthusiasm (accessed October 3, 2010).

2. "A quality decision is a decision backed by much consideration and calculation of the effort that will be required to carry it out to the end. It is a determined decision that cannot be defeated by past failure or temptation. It cannot be altered by circumstance. It is as strong as the person who makes it. The quality decision is an 'I can' decision, backed by words of self-assurance and faith. It sees the desired result well before it can be seen in reality, giving it the strength to endure heavy contradiction," author unknown.

9—Keys to Setting and Achieving Your Goals

1. "Until one is committed, there is hesitancy, the chance to draw back, always ineffectiveness. Concerning all acts of initiative (and creation) there is one elementary truth, the ignorance of which kills countless ideas and splendid plans: that the moment one definitely commits oneself, then Providence moves too. All sorts of things occur to help one that would never otherwise have occurred. A whole stream of events issues from the decision, raising in one's favor all manner of unforeseen incidents and meetings and material assistance, which no man could have dreamed would have come his way," W. H. Murray, *The Scottish Himalayan Expedition* (London: J.M. Dent & Sons, 1951).

2. *God's Little Devotional Book on Success* (Colorado Springs: Honor Books, 1997), 241.

3. Habbakkuk's response to dismal circumstances and the response of Paul and Silas to dismal circumstances were very similar. Habakkuk sang and praised God; six hundred years later Paul and Silas sang and praised God after they had been stripped, beaten, and placed in prison (Acts 16:25). The similar actions of Habakkuk, Paul, and Silas received similar responses—results!

10—THE POWER WITHIN YOU

1. You can learn more about how the Holy Spirit can help you in every area of your life by ordering the CD series *The Role of the Holy Spirit in the New Creation* from www.beyondpositive-thinking.org.

BIBLIOGRAPHY

Blackaby, Henry, and Richard Blackaby. *Spiritual Leadership*. Nashville: Broadman & Holman, 2001.

Bowman, Robert M. Jr. *The Word-Faith Controversy*. Grand Rapids, MI: Baker Books, 2001.

Brant, Roxanne. *Ministering to the Lord*. New Kensington, PA: Whitaker House, 1973.

Burg, Bob. *Winning Without Intimidation*. Jupiter, FL: Samark, 1988.

Canfield, Jack, and Mark Victor Hansen. *Chicken Soup for the Soul Living Your Dreams*. Deerfield Beach, FL: Health Communications, 2003.

Carrin, Charles. *The Edge of Glory*. Lake Mary, FL: Creation House, 2001.

Cho, David Yonggi. *The Fourth Dimension,* Vol. 2. Alachua, FL: Bridge Logos, 1983.

Cloud, Henry. *9 Things You Simply Must Do*. Nashville: Thomas Nelson, 2004.

Colbert, Don. *Deadly Emotions*. Nashville: Thomas Nelson, 2003.

Collins, Jim. *A Brand New You*. Jupiter, FL: Beyond Positive Thinking Ministries, 2006.

———. *The Two Most Outstanding Characteristics of Mankind*. Jupiter, FL: Beyond Positive Thinking Ministries, 2004.

Coy, Bob. *Dreamality*. West Monroe, LA: Howard, 2005.

Friedel, Dewey. *Imagine That!* Shippensburg, PA: Destiny Image, 2006.

Garlow, James L., and Rick Marschall. *The Secret Revealed*. Nashville, TN: Faith Words, 2007.

God's Little Devotional Book on Success. Colorado Springs: Honor Books, 1997.

Gungor, Ed. *There is More to the Secret*. Nashville: Thomas Nelson, 2007.

Hagee, John. *The Seven Secrets*. Lake Mary, FL: Charisma House, 2004.

Hagin, Kenneth. *Classic Sermons*. Tulsa, OK: Faith Library, 1992.

———. *Love: The Way to Victory*. Tulsa, OK: Faith Library, 1994.

———. *Right and Wrong Thinking*. Tulsa, OK: Faith Library, 1986.

———. *Zoe: The God-kind of Life*. Tulsa, OK: Faith Library, 1981.

Halley's Bible Handbook. Grand Rapids, MI: Zondervan, 2000.

Hammond, Mac. *Doorways to Deception.* Minneapolis: Mac Hammond Ministries, 2005.

Harrison, Bob. *Power Points for Success.* New Kensington, PA: Whitaker House, 2005.

Hinn, Benny. *Good Morning Holy Spirit.* Nashville: Thomas Nelson, 1990.

Johnson, Bill. *When Heaven Invades Earth.* O Fallon, MO: Treasure House, 2003.

Jones, Laurie Beth. *Jesus, Life Coach.* New York: MJF Books, 2004.

Kenyon, E. W. *The Hidden Man.* Lynnwood, WA: Kenyon's Gospel Publishing Society, 1970.

———. *New Creation Realities.* Lynnwood, WA: Kenyon's Gospel Publishing Society, 1964.

———. *The New Kind of Love.* Lynnwood, WA: Kenyon's Gospel Publishing Society, 1969.

Kendall, R. T. *Total Forgiveness.* Lake Mary, FL: Charisma House, 2002.

Maxwell, John. *Leadership Gold.* Nashville: Thomas Nelson, 2008.

———. *Put Your Dream to the Test.* Nashville: Thomas Nelson, 2009.

———. *Talent Is Never Enough.* Nashville: Thomas Nelson, 2007.

McDowell, Josh D. *The New Evidence that Demands a Verdict.* Nashville: Thomas Nelson, 1999.

McVeigh, Kate. *7 Habits of Uncommon Achievers.* Tulsa, OK: Faith Library, 2005.

Meyer, Joyce. *Me and My Big Mouth.* New York: Warner Books, 1997.

Meyer, Paul J. *24 Keys That Bring Complete Success.* Alachua, FL: Bridge Logos, 2006.

Motyer, J. A. *The Test of Faith.* Nashville: Serendipity House, 1988.

Munroe, Myles. *Applying the Kingdom.* Shippensburg, PA: Destiny Image, 2007.

———. *The Most Important Person on Earth.* New Kensington, PA: Whitaker House, 2007.

———. *The Power of Vision.* New Kensington, PA: Whitaker House, 2003.

Murdock, Mike. *Dream-Seeds.* Fort Worth, TX: The Wisdom Center, 1986.

————. *The Law of Recognition*. Fort Worth, TX: Wisdom International, 1999.

Osteen, Joel. *Your Best Life Now*. Nashville: Warner Faith, 2004.

Oxford Guide to the Bible. New York: Oxford University Press, 1993.

Price, Frederick K. C. *Faith, Foolishness, or Presumption?* Tulsa, OK: Harrison House, 1979.

Scott, Steven K. *The Richest Man Who Ever Lived*. Garden City, NY: Doubleday, 2006.

Strong's Exhaustive Concordance of the Bible. Gordonsville, TN: Dugan, n.d.

Swindoll, Charles R. *The Quest for Character*. Portland, OR: Multnomah Press, 1990.

Vine's Complete Expository Dictionary of Old and New Testament Words. Nashville: Thomas Nelson, 1996.

Warren, Rick. *The Purpose Driven Life*. Grand Rapids, MI: Zondervan, 2002.

Wommack, Andrew. *You've Already Got It!* Tulsa, OK: Harrison House, 2006.

ABOUT THE AUTHOR

Jim Collins is a pastor, motivational speaker, businessman, and author. Jim is an ordained minister with Gospel Crusade Ministerial Fellowship and pastor of Victory in Christ International in Jupiter, Florida.

After reading and listening to hundreds of motivational books, tapes, and CDs, Jim found that the principles the positive thinking gurus were espousing were simply biblical truths that would work for anyone who applied them. Jim set out to teach these success principles and Beyond Positive Thinking Ministries was born.

Beyond Positive Thinking Ministries conducts motivational and inspirational seminars and workshops for churches, businesses, associations, and civic organizations that focus on success and motivation in the scriptures.

To schedule Jim to come to your church, business, or organization and share these life-changing ideas with your group, please contact:

Beyond Positive Thinking Ministries
4300 S. US Highway One, Suite 203-122
Jupiter, FL 33477
561-262-7676

To order books and CDs:
www.beyondpositivethinking.org

Audio Message
"3 Keys to Prosperity and Success"

Audio Message
"What is Good Success?"

"In Him" Scriptures

"I AM" Affirmations

Success Scripture of the Week E-zine

1. Choose a Location

Identify a location that will accommodate your group and the number of people attending.
(Some suggestions include your church, your business, community clubhouse, local community center, etc.)

2. Choose a Day

Beyond Positive Thinking Success Seminars are typically held on a weeknight from 7–9 p.m. or on Saturday morning from 10 a.m.–12 p.m.

3. Choose a Topic

Seminar topics include:

- Realizing Your God-Given Dream
- Kingdom Success Principles
- Attitudes of Success
- The Business Success Formula
  (Great for Network Marketing)
- Custom Success Seminar
  (Topic of Your Choice)

Jim Collins
Pastor, Motivational Speaker, Businessman, and Author

Jim was the featured speaker at our Annual Educator's Training Seminar and, needless to say, the response was overwhelming! Presenting God's truth in a format that was not only motivating, but practical as well, Jim's message has resounded even today among our staff.

—Jack Wells, Executive Director
School Life
West Palm Beach, FL

I am so grateful for the relationship that we established from you speaking at our Dream Giver Retreat. The Arbonne consultants in attendance really got to see how their dreams could become a reality. I still hear from some of them about how that event affected their outlook on life and what it did for their business.

—Michelle Howe
Independent Consultant
National Vice President

It is my delight to recommend the ministry of Jim Collins. His anointing is a powerful blend of teaching, preaching, and coaching as he shares vital principles of faith, success, and motivation. You can see his heart for people and his desire to help empower people into their purpose and destiny.

—Dr. Rick Kendall
The Body Network
www.bodynetwork.org

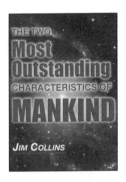

Messages on Audio CD
Recorded LIVE!

1. Are You a Wise Builder?
2. Are You a Wise Master Builder?
3. Are You Saved? Why?
4. The Attitude of Forgiveness
5. The Attitude of Gratitude
6. Christ in You the Hope of Glory
7. Christmas Message
8. The Discipline of Walking in Love
9. Do You Believe in the Resurrection?
10. Do You Know God as My Father?
11. Experiencing God's Power
12. Faith that Receives
13. Faith that Saves
14. Forgiveness Brings Healing
15. God's Covenant Economy
16. God's Will is Prosperity and Health
17. God Wants You Wealthy and Well
18. Healing Scriptures
19. Hearing and Understanding God's Word
20. How to Deal with the Storms of Life
21. How to Fulfill Your Destiny
22. How to Keep Your Healing
23. Is Jesus Lord of Your Time, Talent, and Treasure?
24. Is Perfection Possible?
25. Is There a Heaven to Gain and a Hell to Shun?
26. Jesus Did It All for You!
27. Jesus Your Advocate
28. Jesus Your High Priest
29. Jesus Your Mediator, Intercessor, and Surety
30. Keys to Authority Demonstrated
31. Keys to Setting and Achieving Your Goals
32. The Kingdom of God is Within You
33. Knowing God
34. The Leadership Seminar
35. Living by the Spirit's Power
36. Living Out the Presence and Power of God
37. The Lord's Prayer in Light of the Epistles
38. Marketplace Ministry
39. Marriage Success Guaranteed!
40. The New Creation
41. The Parable of the Talents
42. Physical Prosperity
43. The Power of the American Flag
44. The Proof of True Ministry
45. Realizing Your God-given Dream
46. Receiving Holy Communion
47. Send Me!
48. Success in Relationships
49. Thanksgiving Message
50. Three Keys to Prosperity and Success
51. Victory Through Adversity
52. Walking in Love
53. What Is Good Success?
54. What Is the Source of Truth for Your Life?
55. What to Do When Life Gets Hard
56. The What and Why of Easter
57. The What and Why of Holy Communion
58. Work, Attitude, Character, and Work Ethic
59. Wow! You Have the Mind of Christ
60. The Year of the Bigger and Better

Order online at www.BeyondPositiveThinking.org
All CDs are $8.00 each
FREE Shipping & Handling